McDougal Littell

Biology

Evolution
Unit 4
Resource Book

McDougal Littell
A HOUGHTON MIFFLIN COMPANY
Evanston, Illinois • Boston • Dallas

ISBN-10 0-618-72528-8

ISBN 978-0-618-72528-1

2 3 4 5 6 7 8 9 - MDO - 10 09 08 07

Evolution
Unit 4 Resource Book

CONTENTS

CHAPTER 12 THE HISTORY OF LIFE

CONTENTS

SECTION
10.1 | EARLY IDEAS ABOUT EVOLUTION
Study Guide

KEY CONCEPT
There were theories of biological and geologic change before Darwin.

VOCABULARY		
evolution	fossil	gradualism
species	catastrophism	uniformitarianism

MAIN IDEA: Early scientists proposed ideas about evolution.

In a phrase, tell what each scientist did to help develop evolutionary theory.

Scientist	Contribution to Evolutionary Theory
1. Linnaeus	
2. Buffon	
3. E. Darwin	
4. Lamarck	

5. What two conditions must be true for a group of animals to be considered the same species?

_____

_____

6. Lamarck's ideas of evolution are known as the inheritance of acquired characteristics. What was incorrect about his theory of how organisms evolve?

_____

_____

7. In the 1700s, many people believed that species were fixed and did not change. How did plant hybridization—a type of crossing that could be observed in experiments—help change this view?

_____

_____

STUDY GUIDE, CONTINUED

MAIN IDEA: Theories of geologic change set the stage for Darwin's theory.

8. Write a description of each theory in the space provided.

Geologic Theory	Description
catastrophism	
gradualism	
uniformitarianism	

Vocabulary Check

9. What word refers to traces of an organism that existed in the past?

_____

10. What is the process of biological change by which descendants come to differ from their ancestors?

_____

11. Events such as volcanoes, floods, and earthquakes are the basis of what geologic theory?

_____

12. What geologic theory can be summarized by the phrase "the present is the key to the past"?

_____

Who's Who

Linnaeus	Lamarck	Buffon	E. Darwin

_____ **13.** Charles Darwin's poetic grandfather

_____ **14.** Thought that a giraffe's long neck evolved from reaching high in trees

_____ **15.** Grouped living organisms into categories based on what they looked like

_____ **16.** Wrote *Histoire Naturelle* (Natural History) in 1749

SECTION
10.1 | EARLY IDEAS ABOUT EVOLUTION
Power Notes

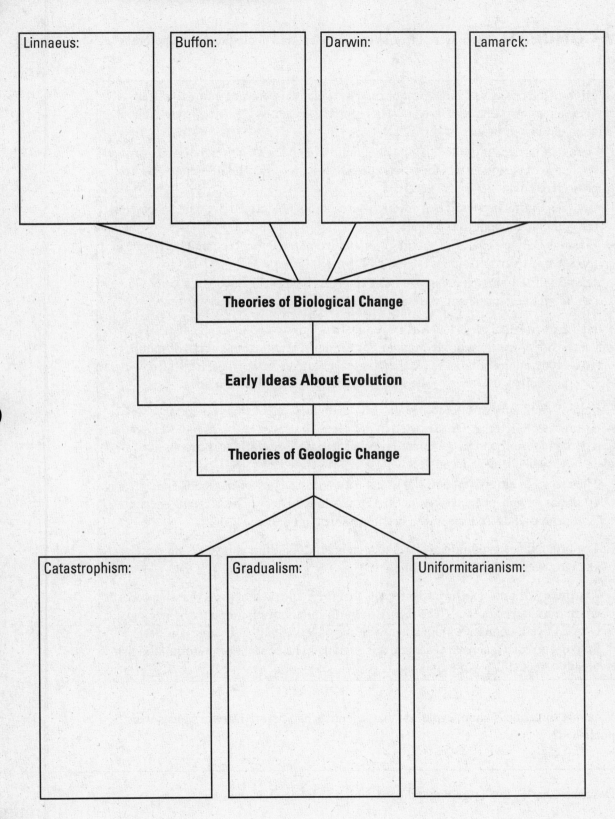

Linnaeus:

Buffon:

Darwin:

Lamarck:

Theories of Biological Change

Early Ideas About Evolution

Theories of Geologic Change

Catastrophism:

Gradualism:

Uniformitarianism:

SECTION 10.1 | EARLY IDEAS ABOUT EVOLUTION
Reinforcement

KEY CONCEPT   There were theories of biological and geologic change before Darwin.

> **Evolution** is the process of biological change by which descendants come to differ from their ancestors. Charles Darwin was not the first scientist to share his ideas about evolution and how it occurs.
>
> - Carolus Linnaeus proposed that plant varieties, or **species**—a group of organisms so similar to one another that they can reproduce and have fertile offspring—can be crossed to create new species.
>
> - Georges Buffon proposed that species shared ancestors instead of arising separately, the common thought of the time.
>
> - Erasmus Darwin, Charles Darwin's grandfather, noted that more-complex forms of life seemed to arise from less-complex forms.
>
> - Jean-Baptiste Lamarck recognized that changes in physical characteristics could be passed on to offspring and were driven by environmental changes over time.
>
> Although Lamarck had ideas that influenced Darwin's thinking, his explanation of how organisms evolve was flawed. He thought, for example, that the long necks of giraffes evolved as generations of giraffes reached for leaves higher in the trees. This idea, which was later discredited, is known as the inheritance of acquired characteristics.
>
> The field of geology also offered insights into evolution. Geologists noted that **fossils**—traces of organisms that existed in the past—in deeper layers of rock were quite different than those found in the upper layers. There were several ideas proposed to explain how such changes occur.
>
> - The theory of **catastrophism** states that natural disasters such as floods and volcanic eruptions have happened often during Earth's long history. These events shaped landforms and caused species to become extinct in the process.
>
> - The principle of **gradualism** states that changes in landforms result from slow changes over a long period of time.
>
> - The theory of **uniformitarianism** states that the geologic processes that shape Earth are uniform through time. The theory of uniformitarianism, proposed by geologist Charles Lyell, combines gradualism with the observation that changes on Earth have occurred at a constant rate and are ongoing. The concept of uniformitarianism greatly affected Darwin's thinking.

1. What are three ideas about evolution that scientists had before Darwin's ideas were published?

_____

2. Describe Charles Lyell's geologic theory, which influenced Darwin.

_____

SECTION
10.2

DARWIN'S OBSERVATIONS
Study Guide

KEY CONCEPT
Darwin's voyage provided insights into evolution.

VOCABULARY
variation
adaptation

MAIN IDEA: Darwin observed differences among island species.

1. What is variation among members of *different* species called?

_____

2. What is variation among members of *the same* species called?

_____

3. What island chain in South America was the source of many of Darwin's insights?

_____

4. Darwin saw populations of various species that seemed well-suited to their environment. What did this suggest?

_____

MAIN IDEA: Darwin observed fossil and geologic evidence supporting an ancient Earth.

5. Darwin observed fossils of huge animals such as *Glyptodon*, a giant armadillo. Why were these fossils of interest to him?

_____

6. Many people in the 1700s thought that Earth was only about 6000 years old. How did the fossil organisms Darwin saw lead him to think Earth must be much older than that?

_____

7. Darwin also observed fossil shells of marine organisms high up in the Andes mountains, and saw an earthquake move land that was underwater above sea level. How did he apply these insights to the evolution of organisms?

_____

8. Look at Figure 10.4 in your textbook. What differences between the two Galápagos tortoises can you identify from the two pictures?

_____

Vocabulary Check

variation	adaptation

_____ **9.** the difference in the physical traits of an individual from those of other individuals in the group to which it belongs

_____ **10.** a feature that allows an organism to better survive in its environment

_____ **11.** A tortoise population lives in an area with high grass. These tortoises have longer necks than tortoises that live in other areas. The long necks are an example of this.

_____ **12.** One bird in a population has a slightly thicker beak than its relatives. This thicker beak is an example of what in the population.

Be Creative

In the space below, draw a sketch of a bird that may eat the food choice that is given in the left column.

Food choice	Sketch
Eats large, hard-shelled nuts	
Eats fruit and insects	

SECTION
10.2

DARWIN'S OBSERVATIONS
Power Notes

Main Idea	Detail Notes
I. Darwin observed variation among island species.	**1.** Variation is: **2.** Examples include tortoises: **3.** and finches:
II. Darwin realized species could adapt to their environment.	**1.** An adaptation is:
III. Darwin observed fossil and geologic evidence of an ancient Earth.	**1.** Fossil evidence included: **2.** Geologic evidence included:

**SECTION
10.2** | DARWIN'S OBSERVATIONS
Reinforcement

KEY CONCEPT Darwin's voyage provided insights into evolution.

Darwin traveled aboard the ship HMS *Beagle* to map the coast of South America and the Pacific Islands in 1831. He observed **variation**—the difference in the physical traits of an individual from those of other individuals in the same population—between island species on his voyage. The differences were especially noticeable on the Galápagos Islands off of South America. Some differences seemed well-suited to the animals' environments and diets. He noticed that species have **adaptations,** or features that allow them to better survive in their environments. Adaptations can lead to genetic change in a population over time.

- Saddle-backed tortoises, which have long necks and legs, lived in areas with a lot of tall plants. Domed tortoises, with their shorter necks and legs, lived in wet areas rich in mosses and short plants.

- Finches with strong, thick beaks lived in areas with a lot of large, hard-shelled nuts. Species of finch with more delicate beaks were found where insects or fruits were widely available.

On his voyage, Darwin also saw fossil evidence of species changing over time.
- He found fossils of huge animals, such as *Glyptodon,* a giant armadillo. He recognized that these fossils looked like living species, which suggested to him that modern animals might have some relationship to fossil forms.
- He observed fossil shells of marine organisms high up in the mountains. Later, Darwin experienced an earthquake and saw firsthand the result: land that had been underwater was moved above sea level.

Darwin realized that over long periods of time, gradual geologic or biological processes can add up to great change.

1. How is a variation different from an adaptation?

_____

_____

_____

2. What are two examples of adaptations that Darwin observed on the Galápagos islands?

_____

_____

3. What did Darwin conclude from the observations he made on his voyage?

_____

_____

SECTION
10.3

THEORY OF NATURAL SELECTION
Study Guide

KEY CONCEPT
Darwin proposed natural selection as a mechanism for evolution.

VOCABULARY		
artificial selection	natural selection	fitness
heritability	population	

MAIN IDEA: Several key insights led to Darwin's idea for natural selection.

1. Why did artificial selection interest Darwin?

_____

_____

2. Why must selected traits be heritable?

_____

_____

3. In natural selection, what must be true of traits that are passed down through generations?

_____

_____

4. What important idea from Thomas Malthus inspired Darwin?

_____

_____

MAIN IDEA: Natural selection explains how evolution can occur.

variation	overproduction	adaptation	descent with modification

_____ 5. producing many offspring, some of which may not survive

_____ 6. individual differences that may be heritable

_____ 7. a structure well-suited for the environment

_____ 8. a heritable trait becoming common in a population

STUDY GUIDE, CONTINUED

Use an organism of your choice to sketch the four principles of natural selection.

9. overproduction	**10.** variation
11. adaptation	**12.** descent with modification

MAIN IDEA: **Natural selection works on existing variation.**

13. Peter and Rosemary Grant observed natural selection acting on traits within a population

of finches on the Galápagos Islands. A drought reduced the number of small soft

seeds but left plenty of large, tough-shelled seeds intact. The next year there was a(n)

_____ (increase, decrease) in the number of large-beaked hatchlings.

14. After several years, the supply of large seeds went down after an unusually wet period.

The increase in small, soft seeds brought a(n) _____ (increase, decrease)

in the number of large-beaked hatchlings the following year.

Vocabulary Check

15. *Humans* are the selective agent in which type of process, artificial selection or natural
selection?

_____

16. *The environment* is the selective agent in which type of process, artificial selection or
natural selection?

_____

17. What is the measure of the ability to survive and produce more offspring relative to
other members of the population called?

_____

18. What is the ability of a trait to be passed down from one generation to the next called?

_____

19. What are all the individuals of a species that live in an area called?

_____

**SECTION
10.3** | THEORY OF NATURAL SELECTION
Power Notes

Artificial selection:

Heritability:

Struggle for survival:

Key insights led to Darwin's theory.

Natural Selection Explains How Evolution Can Occur.

Natural selection is:

The 4 main principles
of natural selection are:

Variation:

Overproduction:

Adaptation:

Descent with
modification:

SECTION 10.3 | THEORY OF NATURAL SELECTION
Reinforcement

KEY CONCEPT   Darwin proposed natural selection as a mechanism for evolution.

Darwin's ideas about evolution were influenced by many different sources. One important influence was the work of farmers and breeders. **Artificial selection,** the process by which humans change a species by breeding it for certain traits, provided Darwin with some important insights. He noticed that breeders could produce a great amount of diversity through selection of certain traits. In order for artificial selection to occur, the trait must be heritable. **Heritability** is the ability of a trait to be inherited, or passed down, from one generation to the next.

Darwin extended the ideas he gained from studying artificial selection to his theory of natural selection. **Natural selection** is a mechanism by which individuals that have inherited beneficial adaptations produce more offspring on average than do other individuals. Unlike artificial selection, where humans do the selecting of traits, in natural selection the environment is the selective agent.

Natural selection is based upon four principles:

- Overproduction: producing more offspring than are likely to survive

- Variation: the heritable differences that exist in every population

- Adaptation: a certain characteristic that allows an individual to survive better than other individuals it competes against for resources

- Descent with modification: the spread of an adaptation throughout new generations

Natural selection works on physical traits rather than genetic material itself. New traits are not made by natural selection. Natural selection can act only on traits that already exist in a population.

1. What is the main *similarity* between the processes of artificial selection and natural selection?

_____

2. What is the main *difference* between artificial selection and natural selection?

_____

3. Could natural selection work on a trait that is not heritable? Explain.

_____

4. Could natural selection work on a population that has no variation? Explain.

_____

SECTION 10.4 | EVIDENCE OF EVOLUTION
Study Guide

KEY CONCEPT
Evidence of common ancestry among species comes from many sources.

VOCABULARY	
biogeography	analogous structure
homologous structure	vestigial structure

MAIN IDEA: Evidence for evolution in Darwin's time came from several sources.

In the diagram below, give examples of each type of evidence for evolution.

1. Fossils:

2. Geography:

Evidence for evolution in Darwin's time came from several sources.

3. Embryology:

4. Anatomy:

MAIN IDEA: Structural patterns are clues to the history of a species.

5. Vestigial structures seem to lack any useful function, or are at least no longer used for their original purpose. Give three examples of vestigial structures.

_____

_____

6. Many modern whale species have vestigial pelvic and leg bones. What does this suggest about the ancestry of modern whales?

_____

Vocabulary Check

homologous structure	analogous structure	vestigial structure

_____ **7.** Feature that is similar in structure in different organisms but has different functions

_____ **8.** Feature that performs a similar function in different organisms but is not similar in origin

_____ **9.** Is *not* evidence of a common ancestor

_____ **10.** Remnant of an organ or structure that had a function in an early ancestor

_____ **11.** Examples include the wing of a bat and the hand of a human

_____ **12.** Examples include the wing of a bird and the wing of an insect

_____ **13.** Examples include the wing of an ostrich and the appendix of a human

Sketch it Out

Use Figure 10.11 to sketch a skeleton of a human hand next to the whale fin skeleton shown below. Draw lines to match the groups of bones that are homologous for these two structures.

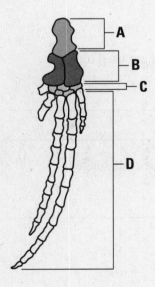

SECTION
10.4
EVIDENCE OF EVOLUTION
Power Notes

Main Idea
Evidence of common ancestry among species comes from many sources.

Fossils:

Geography:

Embryology:

Anatomy:

Analogous structures are not evidence of a recent common ancestor.

Analogous structures:

Homologous structures:

Vestigial structures:

SECTION 10.4 | EVIDENCE OF EVOLUTION
Reinforcement

KEY CONCEPT Evidence of common ancestry among species comes from many sources.

Darwin found evidence supporting evolution from a wide range of sources. The most important and convincing support came from fossils, geography, embryology, and anatomy.

- The fossil is a record of change in a species over time. Geologists found that fossil organisms on the bottom, or older, layers were more primitive than those in the upper, or newer, layers. These findings supported Darwin's concept of descent with modification.

- **Biogeography,** the study of the distribution of organisms around the world, reveals a pattern of evolution of organisms. Darwin's observations on the Galapagos islands, for instance, demonstrated that species can adapt to different environments and evolve into separate populations or species over time.

- Embryology, the study of embryo development, reveals that even organisms that are very different from each other in their adult forms can have similar patterns of development. Two species that exhibit similar traits during development are likely to have a common ancestor.

- Anatomy also provides insight into evolution. **Homologous structures** are features that are similar in structure but appear in different organisms and have different functions. **Vestigial structures** are remnants of organs or structures that had a function in an early ancestor. Both homologous structures and vestigial structures point to a shared ancestry among organisms that share them.

1. How did the study of fossils help support Darwin's ideas about evolution?

_____

_____

2. How did the study of organisms on islands help support Darwin's ideas?

_____

3. In all animals with backbones, including humans, early embryos have gill slits that later develop into structures of ears and throats in mammals. What does this suggest about the relationship between all vertebrates?

_____

4. What are two examples of types of body structures that provide evidence of a common ancestor among diverse organisms?

_____

SECTION
10.5

EVOLUTIONARY BIOLOGY TODAY
Study Guide

KEY CONCEPT
New technology is furthering our understanding of
evolution.

VOCABULARY
paleontology

MAIN IDEA: Fossils provide a record of evolution.

1. What are two reasons that the fossil record is not complete?

_____

2. What is one example of a transitional fossil that has been found?

_____

3. Why are transitional fossils important?

_____

MAIN IDEA: Molecular and genetic evidence support fossil and anatomical evidence.

In a phrase, explain how each of the following contribute to evolutionary theory.

Molecular Evidence	Contribution to Evolutionary Theory
4. DNA sequence analysis	
5. Pseudogenes	
6. Homeobox genes	
7. Protein comparisons	

STUDY GUIDE, CONTINUED

MAIN IDEA: **Evolution unites all fields of biology.**

8. What two things combine to make up our modern evolutionary theory?

_____

_____

9. How has molecular evidence helped support fossil evidence in determining the early ancestor of modern-day whales?

_____

10. What is meant by the phrase "Evolution unites all fields of biology"?

_____

Vocabulary Check

11. How does paleontology contribute to evolutionary biology?

_____

_____

Sketch it Out

Look at the fossil evidence of whale evolution shown in Figure 10.16. Sketch one part of the skeletons (such as the skull, forelimbs, hindlimbs, or ribcages) of each of the whale ancestors. Briefly describe their differences and propose how these differences are well-suited for the habitat in which the animals lived.

**SECTION
10.5**

EVOLUTIONARY BIOLOGY TODAY
Power Notes

DNA sequence analysis:

Pseudogenes:

**New technology is furthering our
understanding of evolution.**

Homeobox genes:

Protein comparisons:

SECTION 10.5 | EVOLUTIONARY BIOLOGY TODAY
Reinforcement

KEY CONCEPT   New technology is furthering our understanding of evolution.

The study of fossils or extinct organisms, called **paleontology,** continues to provide new information and support current hypotheses about how evolution occurs. The fossil record, although incomplete, contains many transitional fossils, or "missing links," that demonstrate the evolution of traits. Transitional fossils can also indicate common ancestors between groups, such as *Basilosaurus isis*, which had a whalelike body but the limbs of a land animal.

Modern molecular techniques continue to provide new information about how evolution occurs. Examples include

- DNA sequence analysis: The more closely related two organisms are, the more similar their DNA will be.

- Pseudogenes: Pseudogenes no longer function but are still carried along with working DNA. They are not affected by natural selection, so common pseudogenes among organisms must reflect a common ancestor.

- Homeobox genes: These genes control the development of structures within the body. They are in diverse organisms, from fruit flies to humans, so they can indicate a very distant common ancestor.

- Protein comparisons: Sometimes known as molecular fingerprinting, this technique is based on the idea that different species that have cells with the same proteins most likely came from a common ancestor.

The theory of natural selection supported by genetic evidence is sometimes called the modern synthesis of evolutionary theory. The amount of data that can be collected by molecular evidence alone is overwhelming. Scientists from many fields of science are contributing to our understanding of evolution, and the field of evolutionary biology is quickly growing. Evolution is a unifying theme among all the fields of biology today.

1. Why is *Basilosauris isis* considered a transitional fossil?

_____

2. What underlying theme do the four molecular techniques share?

_____

_____

3. What is the modern synthesis of evolutionary theory?

_____

_____

CHAPTER 10
Principles of Evolution

CHAPTER 10 | INTERPRETING LINE GRAPHS
Data Analysis Practice

Data from experiments can be represented in a line graph for analysis and interpretation.

Scientists breeding salmon in captivity can artificially select traits such as large body size and females that produce many eggs. Scientists have determined that one of the effects of artificially selecting these traits is the production of eggs with a smaller volume. In some areas, salmon that have been bred in captivity are added to rivers to help increase population levels. Once released, the previously captive salmon breed with the wild salmon.

Scientists hypothesized that in rivers that had significant percentages of captive salmon being added, there would be rapid evolution toward smaller egg size in future generations of salmon. Scientists collected data in four rivers in British Columbia, Canada, to test the hypothesis. Over the course of the study, body size in females did not change. The graph below shows the results of the study.

GRAPH 1. EGG VOLUME OVER TIME

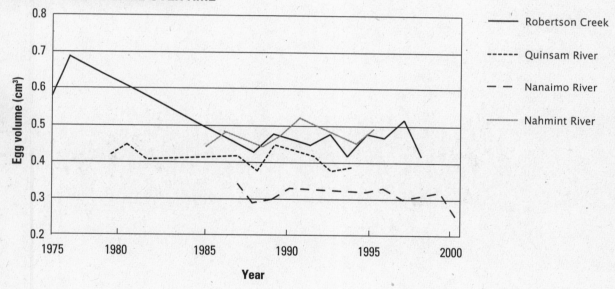

1. **Analyze** Less than 20% of the Nahmint and Nanaimo Rivers were stocked with captive bred salmon. Was there a decrease in egg size in these rivers?

_____

2. **Analyze** More than 25% of the fish in the Quinsam River and Robertson Creek were captive bred. Was there a decrease in egg size in either place?

_____

_____

3. **Conclude** How does stocking rivers with salmon bred in captivity affect egg size?

_____

LYSENKOISM: EVOLUTIONARY THEORY IN THE U.S.S.R.
Pre-AP* Activity

*Pre-AP is a registered trademark of the College Board, which was not involved in the production of and does not endorse this product.

You have learned in Chapter 10 that Charles Darwin proposed that individuals with characteristics that prove to be beneficial in their environment are more likely to survive and produce offspring than less well adapted individuals. As you learned, Lamarck had seen a connection between the environment and beneficial variations in traits. Though it was rejected by the scientific community, Lamarckism was reexamined on occasion—especially when Darwin's theory of natural selection posed a threat to political ideologies.

THE RETURN OF LAMARCK

In the early 20th century, exciting discoveries on the mechanism of inheritance were emerging in Germany and the United States. Despite advances in the understanding of heritability, some scientists continued to favor Lamarck's theory. A leading proponent of this in the Soviet Union was a plant breeder named Trofim Denisovich Lysenko (1898–1976). Though not a trained scientist, Lysenko rose to prominence through his fierce advocacy of an anti-intellectual worldview that interpreted science through Soviet ideology. Lysenko molded Lamarckism into a theory that viewed heritability and other aspects of biology through the lens of Soviet communism.

Lysenko's rise to prominence came from his ability to do quick experiments at a time when the Soviet government was impatient for results, particularly in agriculture. The scientific method, including replicating controlled studies and objective analysis, took too long. Lysenko provided "results" quickly by using small sample sizes, rarely using controls, and avoiding replicated studies. His results drew attention for their speedy and their apparent success, which Lysenko guaranteed by reporting only successes.

"THE SITUATION IN THE SCIENCE OF BIOLOGY"—1948

The remarks below are excerpted from an address delivered by Lysenko at a conference in 1948. The scientists to whom he referred included August Weismann, the German biologist who distinguished between somatic cells and germline cells, Gregor Mendel, and Thomas Morgan, whose studies of fruit fly chromosomes later earned a Nobel prize.

The materialist theory of the evolution of living nature involves recognition of the necessity of hereditary transmission of individual characteristics acquired by the organism under the conditions of its life; it is unthinkable without recognition of the inheritance of acquired characters. [Other scientists] denied the inheritability of acquired characters and elaborated the idea of a special hereditary substance to be sought for in the nucleus. . . . [They] contend that the chromosomes contain a special "hereditary substance" which resides in the body of the organism as if in a case and is transmitted to coming generations irrespective of the qualitative features of the body and its conditions of life. The conclusion drawn . . . is that new tendencies and characteristics acquired by the organism under the influence of conditions . . . are not inherited and can have no evolutionary significance . . . . According to this theory, characters acquired by vegetable and animal organisms cannot be handed down, are not inherited.

LYSENKO AND DARWIN'S "STRUGGLE FOR EXISTENCE"

Of the many tenets of Darwin's theory of natural selection that Lysenko disliked, few were more contemptible to him than the views of Malthus on the natural limits to population size and the resultant struggle for existence between members of a population.

All mankind belongs to one biological species. Hence, bourgeois science had to invent intraspecific struggle. In nature, they say, within each species there is a cruel struggle for food . . . The stronger, better-adapted individuals are the victors. The same . . . occurs among people: the capitalists have millions, the workers live in poverty, because the capitalists supposedly are more intelligent and more able because of their heredity . . . We Soviet people know well that the oppression of the workers, the dominance of the capitalist class . . . are all based on the laws of a rotting, moribund, bourgeois, capitalist society . . . There is no intraspecific competition in nature. There is only competition between species: the wolf eats the hare; the hare does not eat another hare, it eats grass.

THE EFFECT OF LYSENKOISM ON SCIENTIFIC THOUGHT

Lysenko's use of "science" to support Soviet ideals, and vice versa, made a deep impression on Joseph Stalin, the Soviet dictator. He made Lysenko the Director of Genetics at the USSR Academy of Sciences in 1935. The standing director, a respected biologist whose views paralleled those in classical genetics, was arrested and imprisoned. The episode sent the message to scientists that if their work conflicted with state-approved theories, they could suffer the same fate. Soviet physicists began to argue against Einstein's theory of relativity, and biologists challenged well-established tenets of microbiology and dropped any visible pursuit of genetic research. Scientific theories that did not fit Soviet ideology were ignored, and many scientists from this period were arrested as enemies of the state and sent to gulags (labor camps) or simply "disappeared." This downward spiral prevailed until Stalin's death in 1952. Though Lysenko retained his prominence under Stalin's successor, Nikita Khruschev, the taboo against criticizing him was lifted. A strongly worded attack on his role in holding back Soviet science was voiced in 1964 by several prominent scientists. Lysenko was removed from his position.

Answer the following questions on a separate piece of paper.

1. Soviet communism stressed the solidarity of the working class and sought to rid the world of a bourgeois, capitalist class. Why then was it important for Lysenko to challenge the Malthusian/Darwinian ideas of limited resources and intraspecific competition? How would those theories pose a threat to communism?

2. Why is an "anti-intellectual" ideology damaging for science?

3. Lysenko once stated that "to obtain a certain result, you must want to obtain precisely that result; if you want to obtain a certain result, you will obtain it . . . I need only such people as will obtain the results I need." In what ways is such a statement in opposition to the scientific method?

CHAPTER 10 | BIOINFORMATICS: SEQUENCING THE CLOCK GENE
Pre-AP Activity

As you have learned in Chapters 9 and 10, advances in genetics and molecular biology have provided new insights into evolution and have led to an explosion of data and biological information. Increased computing power and the development of extensive databases of information have led to a new field of study: bioinformatics. Bioinformatics is an invaluable tool in evolutionary biology. It has enabled scientists to compare and analyze the DNA sequences specifically associated with genes such as the clock gene in humans and mice, as you will see below.

DATABASES AND BIOINFORMATICS

When large amounts of scientific data and information are generated, it must be organized in such a way that other scientists have access to it. Most scientific data and information are stored in databases. A database is a computerized collection of data that stores, organizes, and indexes data so that they can be located and retrieved quickly. One such database is the National Institutes of Health's genetic sequence database, GenBank, which contains all publicly available DNA sequences.

Due to the nature of some of the data, it may have to be manipulated. Bioinformatics is the branch of science that integrates biology, computer science, and information technology to analyze biological data such as genetic codes, experimental results, taxonomy trees, patient statistics, and scientific literature. Bioinformatics allows scientists to access genetic sequences for various organisms and uncover evolutionary relationships between them. As you have learned, the closer the sequences are, the more closely the organisms are related.

CLOCK GENES

Most organisms have evolved an internal biological clock, also known as the circadian rhythm, to adapt to the changes that take place over the course of a day and sometimes over the course of a year. An organism's circadian rhythm controls its activity patterns in relation to light and dark, such as when it sleeps and when it awakens. The circadian rhythm is also responsible for other biological functions: body temperature, metabolism, blood pressure, hormone secretion, heart activity, oxygen consumption, hibernation, and migration.

The circadian rhythm in mammals is controlled by clock genes. Clock genes carry the genetic instructions to produce specific proteins. By increasing or decreasing protein levels throughout the day, clock genes directly affect the circadian rhythm. The first mammalian clock gene was discovered in a mouse in 1997. Scientists identified the location of the gene and determined its sequence. In 2001, scientists at the University of Utah discovered the first human clock gene. Using databases such as GenBank, scientists have been able to analyze and compare the DNA sequences for the clock gene in humans and mice. In doing so, scientists have established that the human clock gene DNA sequence extends for 2538 base pairs and is 89% identical to that of the mouse. The sequence of the 846 amino acids produced by those base pairs is 96% identical to the amino acid sequence produced in mice.

On the next page, you will compare the beginning of the DNA sequences of the clock genes of humans and mice. Note that each sequence is broken into five segments in order to fit on the page.

CHAPTER 10
Principles of Evolution

CLOCK GENE DNA SEQUENCES

Human	atgttgttta	ccgtaagctg	tagtaaaatg	agctcgattg	ttgacagaga
Mouse	atggtgttta	ccgtaagctg	tagtaaaatg	agctcaattg	ttgacagaga
Human	tgacagtagt	atttttgatg	ggttggtgga	agaagatgac	aaggacaaag
Mouse	tgacagtagt	atttttgatg	gattggtgga	agaagatgac	aaggacaaag
Human	cgaaaagagt	atctagaaac	aaatctgaaa	agaaacgtag	agatcaattt
Mouse	caaaaagagt	atctagaaac	aaatcagaaa	agaaacgtag	agatcagttc
Human	aatgttctca	ttaaagaact	gggatccatg	cttcctggta	atgctagaaa
Mouse	aatgtcctca	ttaaggagct	ggggtctatg	cttcctggta	acgcgagaaa
Human	gatggacaaa	tctactgttc	tgcagaaaag	cattgatttt	ttacgaaaac
Mouse	gatggacaag	tctactgttc	tacagaagag	cattgatttt	ttgcgcaaac

Answer the following questions on a separate sheet of paper.

1. Using the DNA sequences above, how many base differences are there between the human and mouse clock gene? Mark the mismatched pairs, then calculate the percentage of similarity between the two sequences.

2. How does the value you calculated compare to the findings of the scientists? What may account for any differences?

3. Scientists have established that the sequences of the human and mouse clock gene are 89% identical, but the sequences of amino acids produced are 96% identical. Explain what might account for this discrepancy.

4. In the first segment of the human clock gene sequence shown above, the following series of amino acids appears:
methionine–leucine–phenylalanine–threonine–valine–serine–cysteine–serine–lysine–methionine
Using Figure 8.13 on page 244, write three different DNA sequences that would still code for those amino acids, in that order.

CHAPTER 10 | PRINCIPLES OF EVOLUTION
Vocabulary Practice

evolution	variation	fitness
species	adaptation	biogeography
fossil	artificial selection	homologous structure
catastrophism	heritability	analogous structure
gradualism	natural selection	vestigial structure
uniformitarianism	population	paleontology

A. Stepped-Out Vocabulary
Determine the vocabulary word that fits best, define each word, or write two additional facts that are related to the word in the spaces below.

WORD	DEFINITION	MORE INFORMATION
Example Fossil	Traces of an organism that existed in the past.	there are different types of fossils
		they allow scientists to study evolution
1. Variation		can occur among members of different species
		can occur among members of the same species
2.	Features that are similar in structure but appear in different organisms and have different functions.	evidence of common descent
		common examples are the forelimbs of vertebrates
3. Analogous structures	Structures that perform a similar function but are not similar in origin.	

VOCABULARY PRACTICE, CONTINUED

WORD	DEFINITION	MORE INFORMATION
4.		evidence for common descent
		examples include snake pelvic bones

B. Compound Word Puzzle Read the phrase and write the word that it most closely describes. Then write another phrase that describes the same word in a different way.

PHRASE 1	WORD	PHRASE 2
Example Process of biological change over time	Evolution	Process by which descendents come to differ from their ancestors
1. Can interbreed and produce fertile offspring		
2. Beneficial feature		
3. The environment is the selective agent		
4. All the individuals of a species that live in an area		

C. Do-It Yourself Matching In a random order, write short definitions for each term on the blank lines to the right. Then give your paper to a classmate who should write the number of the term next to the correct definition.

1. evolution   ____ _____

2. fitness   ____ _____

3. catastrophism   ____ _____

4. gradualism   ____ _____

VOCABULARY PRACTICE, CONTINUED

5. uniformitarianism _____ _____

6. artificial selection _____ _____

7. natural selection _____ _____

8. paleontology _____ _____

9. biogeography _____ _____

10. heritability _____ _____

D. Find the Odd Word Put a checkmark next to the word that does not belong and explain why. There may be more than one correct way to answer for some of the word sets.

1. _____ fossil   Explanation_____

_____ fitness   _____

_____ paleontology

2. _____ artificial selection   Explanation_____

_____ heritability   _____

_____ biogeography

3. _____ catastrophism   Explanation_____

_____ gradualism   _____

_____ uniformitarianism

4. _____ homologous structure   Explanation_____

_____ analogous structure   _____

_____ vestigial structure

5. _____ variation   Explanation_____

_____ adaptation   _____

_____ vestigial structure

6. _____ evolution   Explanation_____

_____ natural selection   _____

_____ catastrophism

VOCABULARY PRACTICE, CONTINUED

E. Crossword Puzzle Use the clues to solve the puzzle.

Across

1. Theory that processes that can be seen today also occurred in the past
5. Remnants of organs that functioned in an ancestor
8. Traces or remains of an organism that existed in the past
10. Features with the same function in two organisms but different recent ancestors
11. Theory of dramatic natural events changing Earth
12. Study of fossils
13. Theory of how evolution occurs
14. Beneficial feature that helps survival

Down

2. Choosing particular traits for breeding
3. Theory of slow change over long time periods
4. Process of biological change over generations
6. Members of a group that can interbreed
7. Measure of ability to survive and produce offspring

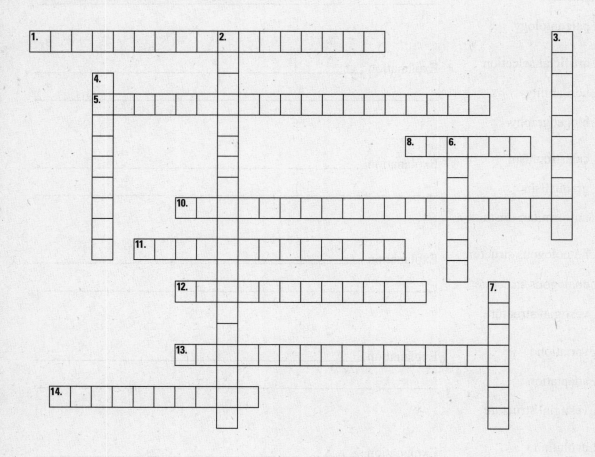

SECTION
11.1
GENETIC VARIATION WITHIN POPULATIONS
Study Guide

KEY CONCEPT

A population shares a common gene pool.

VOCABULARY
gene pool
allele frequency

MAIN IDEA: Genetic variation in a population increases the chance that some individuals will survive.

1. What kind of variation must exist in a population that has a wide range of phenotypes?

   _____

2. How can a wide range of phenotypes increase the chance that some individuals will survive in a changing environment?

   _____

   _____

Fill in the concept map below.

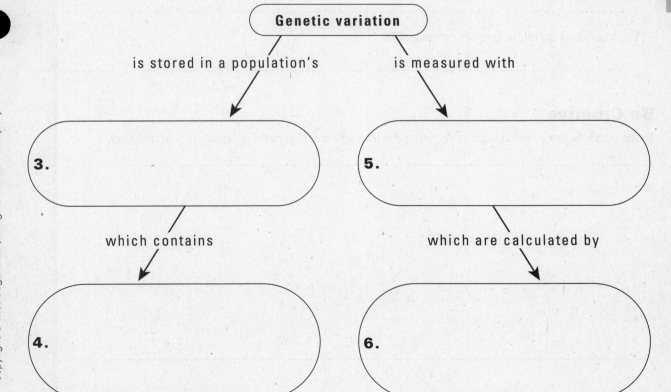

Genetic variation

is stored in a population's

is measured with

3. _____

5. _____

which contains

which are calculated by

4. _____

6. _____

STUDY GUIDE, CONTINUED

MAIN IDEA: **Genetic variation comes from several sources.**

In a phrase, describe how each term below provides a source of genetic variation.

Source	How It Provides Genetic Variation
7. mutation	
8. recombination	
9. hybridization	

Vocabulary Check

10. How is a gene pool like a pool of genes?

_____

11. What does an allele frequency measure?

_____

Be Creative

In the space below, write a logo advertising the importance of genetic diversity to a population.

SECTION 11.1 | GENETIC VARIATION WITHIN POPULATIONS
Power Notes

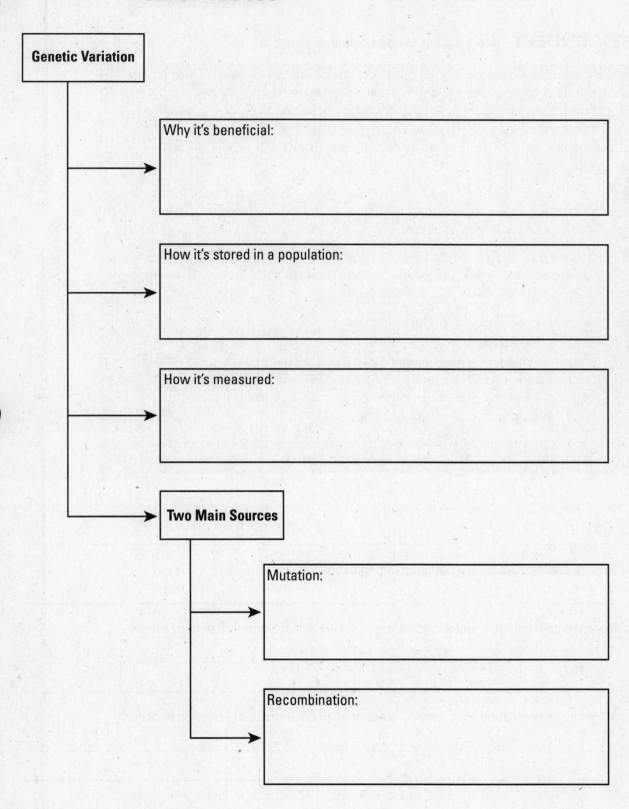

Genetic Variation

Why it's beneficial:

How it's stored in a population:

How it's measured:

Two Main Sources

Mutation:

Recombination:

SECTION
11.1

GENETIC VARIATION WITHIN POPULATIONS
Reinforcement

KEY CONCEPT   A population shares a common gene pool.

In most populations, individuals have different characteristics, or traits. A phenotype is a trait produced by one or more genes, and a single population may have a range of phenotypes for any given trait. In order for natural selection to occur, a population must have different phenotypes to be selected for or against. In this way, a variety of phenotypes makes it more likely that certain individuals will survive different environmental pressures.

In order for a population to have a variety of phenotypes, it must have genetic variation. Genetic variation comes in the form of different alleles for any given gene. A population's **gene pool** is the combined alleles of all the individuals in a population.

Biologists measure the genetic diversity of a population by calculating the frequencies, or rates, of each allele in the gene pool. An **allele frequency** is therefore a measure of how common a certain allele is in the gene pool.

Genetic variation comes from two main sources:
- Mutations are random changes in DNA. Some mutations cause a new allele to form. If a mutation occurs in a reproductive cell, it can be passed on to offspring.
- Recombination is a process in which new allele combinations can form in offspring. Most recombination occurs during meiosis, when the alleles in each parent's gametes are arranged in new ways.

Some biologists are studying hybridization as another source of genetic variation. Hybridization occurs when individuals of two related but different species mate.

1. What makes up a population's gene pool?

_____

2. How is genetic variation measured in a population?

_____

3. Describe how mutation and recombination provide genetic variation to populations.

_____

_____

4. Why must a population have genetic variation in order for natural selection to occur?

_____

_____

_____

SECTION
11.2 | NATURAL SELECTION IN POPULATIONS
Study Guide

KEY CONCEPT
Populations, not individuals, evolve.

VOCABULARY	
normal distribution	stabilizing selection
microevolution	disruptive selection
directional selection	

MAIN IDEA: **Natural selection acts on a distribution of traits.**

1. What is a phenotypic distribution?

_____

2. What can you learn from looking at a phenotypic distribution?

_____

_____

3. In a population that is not undergoing natural selection for a certain trait, what does the phenotypic distribution look like?

_____

In the space provided below, draw the phenotypic distribution for a trait that follows a normal distribution. Be sure to label the axes as well as the mean phenotype.

STUDY GUIDE, CONTINUED

MAIN IDEA: Natural selection can change the distribution of a trait in one of three ways.

In the table below, take notes about the three patterns of natural selection.

Type of Selection	How It Works	Graph
4. directional selection		
5. stabilizing selection		
6. disruptive selection		

Vocabulary Check

7. The observable change in _____ over time is called microevolution.

8. During _____ selection, the intermediate phenotype is selected for.

9. During _____ selection, both extreme phenotypes are selected for.

10. During _____ selection, the mean phenotype changes.

SECTION
11.2

NATURAL SELECTION IN POPULATIONS
Power Notes

Normal distribution:

A population follows a normal
distribution when:

Frequency

Range of variable

Microevolution:

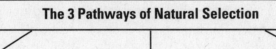

The 3 Pathways of Natural Selection

Directional selection:

_____

_____

_____

Frequency

Range of variable

Example:

Stabilizing selection:

_____

_____

_____

Frequency

Range of variable

Example:

Disruptive selection:

_____

_____

_____

Frequency

Range of variable

Example:

SECTION 11.2 | NATURAL SELECTION IN POPULATIONS
Reinforcement

KEY CONCEPT   Populations, not individuals, evolve.

The phenotypes for a certain trait in a population can be graphed in what is called a phenotypic distribution. In this type of graph, you can see the range of phenotypes present in the population. You can also see how common each of these phenotypes is in the population, as measured by its frequency.

For a trait that is not undergoing natural selection, the intermediate phenotype is the most common phenotype in the population, while the extreme phenotypes are less common. A frequency distribution for this type of trait looks like a bell-shaped curve. A type of distribution in which the frequency is highest near the mean and decreases toward each extreme is called a **normal distribution.**

Natural selection can cause a phenotypic distribution to change in one of three ways:
*   **Directional selection** favors phenotypes at one extreme of a trait's range. This type of selection causes the entire bell-shaped curve to shift in one direction or the other, toward the phenotype that is advantageous. During directional selection, the mean (or average) phenotype changes.
*   **Stabilizing selection** favors intermediate phenotypes, selecting against phenotypes at both extremes of a trait's range. This type of selection causes the peak of the bell-shaped curve to become taller and more narrow (more "stable"), since the intermediate phenotype is becoming more and more common in the population.
*   **Disruptive selection** favors phenotypes at both extreme's of a trait's range, selecting against intermediate phenotypes. This type of selection disrupts the distribution by causing a "dip" in the center of the bell-shaped curve, since the intermediate phenotype is becoming less and less common in the population.

1. What is shown in a phenotypic distribution?

   _____

2. In what type of situation does a phenotypic distribution look like a bell-shaped curve?

   _____

3. What is a normal distribution?

   _____

4. Name and describe the three ways in which natural selection can change the distribution of a trait.

   _____

   _____

   _____

KEY CONCEPT

Natural selection is not the only mechanism through which populations evolve.

VOCABULARY		
gene flow	bottleneck effect	sexual selection
genetic drift	founder effect	

MAIN IDEA: **Gene flow is the movement of alleles between populations.**

Fill in the word or phrase that best completes each statement.

1. When an individual _____ from its population, its alleles are no longer part of that population's gene pool.

2. When an individual _____ into a new population, the genetic diversity of this new population increases.

3. Gene flow among neighboring populations helps to keep the _____ of these populations similar.

MAIN IDEA: **Genetic drift can occur in small populations.**

4. How is genetic drift different from natural selection?

_____

_____

Use Y-notes to compare and contrast the bottleneck effect and the founder effect.

Bottleneck effect
_____
_____
_____
_____

Founder effect
_____
_____
_____
_____

Both
_____
_____
_____
_____

CHAPTER 11
The Evolution of Populations

5. Why is genetic drift more likely to occur in smaller populations?

_____

_____

6. What are some problems that can result from genetic drift?

_____

_____

MAIN IDEA: Sexual selection is a source of evolutionary change.

7. Why is the cost of reproduction different for males and females?

_____

_____

8. What is sexual selection?

_____

_____

9. _____ selection involves fighting among males for a female,

whereas _____ selection involves males displaying traits

to impress females.

Vocabulary Check

In the spaces provided below, draw pictures that help you to remember the definitions of the vocabulary words.

Gene Flow	Bottleneck Effect	Founder Effect

SECTION
11.3 | OTHER MECHANISMS OF EVOLUTION
Power Notes

Gene Flow

Definition:

How it works:

Lots of gene flow
between populations   results in ⇒

Limited gene flow
between populations   results in ⇒

Genetic Drift

Definition:

How it works:

Key Terms

   Bottleneck effect:

   Founder effect:

Negative effects:

Sexual Selection

Definition:

How it works:

Types

   Intrasexual:

   Intersexual:

CHAPTER 11
The Evolution of Populations

SECTION
11.3
OTHER MECHANISMS OF EVOLUTION
Reinforcement

KEY CONCEPT   Natural selection is not the only mechanism through which populations evolve.

Three other mechanisms through which populations can evolve are gene flow, genetic drift, and sexual selection.

Gene flow is the movement of alleles between populations. When individuals of one population leave that population to join a new one, they take their alleles with them. Emigration is the process of leaving a population and immigration is the process of joining a new population. Gene flow between neighboring populations helps to keep their gene pools similar. However, if gene flow between such populations stops, they will become more and more genetically different.

Genetic drift accounts for changes in allele frequencies that are due to chance. Smaller populations are more affected by genetic drift because there are less alleles to "balance out" the effect of random changes. Due to chance alone, some alleles will likely become more common, while others will become less common and eventually disappear. Genetic drift therefore decreases genetic variation in a population. Two situations commonly cause populations to become small enough for genetic drift to occur.

- During the **bottleneck effect,** genetic drift occurs after an event drastically reduces the size of a population.
- During the **founder effect,** genetic drift occurs after a small number of individuals colonize a new area, starting a new population.

Sexual selection occurs when certain traits increase mating success, as a result of females being choosy about their potential mates. This drives competition among males to mate with quality females. During intrasexual selection, males fight with each other for the right to mate with a female. During intersexual selection, males display certain traits to try to impress females. Traits that help males to win mates become selected for generation after generation. Over time, these traits can become highly exaggerated, such as the brightly-colored tail feathers of peacocks.

1. How can gene flow result in changes in allele frequencies?

_____

_____

2. Why are smaller populations more affected by genetic drift?

_____

3. How can sexual selection lead to highly exaggerated traits among males?

_____

_____

SECTION
11.4 | HARDY-WEINBERG EQUILIBRIUM
Study Guide

KEY CONCEPT
Hardy-Weinberg equilibrium provides a framework for understanding how populations evolve.

VOCABULARY
Hardy-Weinberg equilibrium

MAIN IDEA: Hardy-Weinberg equilibrium describes populations that are not evolving.

1. What variable remains constant, or in equilibrium, in the Hardy-Weinberg model?

_____

2. Name the five conditions required for a population to be in Hardy-Weinberg equilibrium.

_____

_____

3. Name two ways that population biologists can use Hardy-Weinberg equilibrium.

_____

_____

MAIN IDEA: The Hardy-Weinberg equation is used to predict genotype frequencies for a population.

4. Write the Hardy-Weinberg equation:

5. Fill in the missing information about the variables involved in the Hardy-Weinberg equation.

Variable	What It Represents
	frequency of dominant homozygous genotype
2pq	
	frequency of recessive homozygous genotype
p	
	frequency of recessive allele

6. In what types of systems can the Hardy-Weinberg equation be used?

_____

7. What variables must be known in order to use the Hardy-Weinberg equation?

_____

8. What can be concluded if real genetic data do not match the frequencies predicted by the equation?

_____

MAIN IDEA: There are five factors that can lead to evolution.

9. Take notes about these five factors in the table below.

Factor	How It Can Lead To Evolution
genetic drift	
gene flow	
mutation	
sexual selection	
natural selection	

Vocabulary Check

10. A population is said to be in Hardy-Weinberg equilibrium for a trait if

_____ stay the same from generation to generation.

SECTION
11.4 | HARDY-WEINBERG EQUILIBRIUM
Power Notes

Copyright © McDougal Littell/Houghton Mifflin Company.

CHAPTER 11
The Evolution of Populations

Hardy-Weinberg equilibrium:

Why is it important:

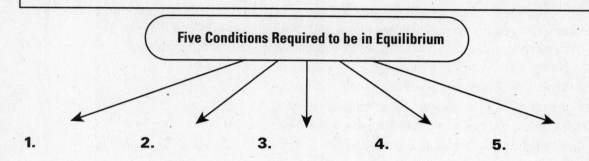

Five Conditions Required to be in Equilibrium

1.   2.   3.   4.   5.

Hardy-Weinberg equation: _____ + _____ + _____ = _____

What it means:

How it is used:

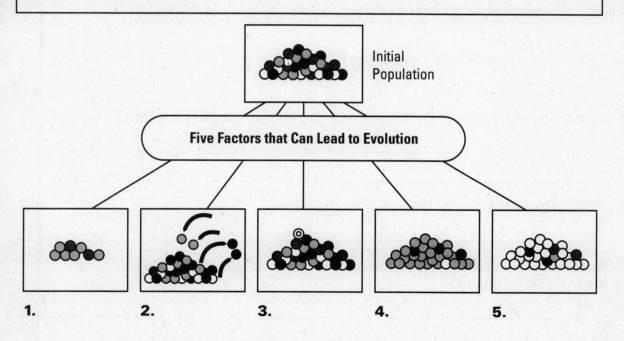

Initial Population

Five Factors that Can Lead to Evolution

1.   2.   3.   4.   5.

SECTION
11.4 | HARDY-WEINBERG EQUILIBRIUM
Reinforcement

KEY CONCEPT Hardy-Weinberg equilibrium provides a framework for understanding how populations evolve.

> The Hardy-Weinberg model shows that if there are no forces of evolution acting on a population, the allele frequencies will remain constant—in equilibrium—from generation to generation. If a real population matches this model, that population is said to be in **Hardy-Weinberg equilibrium.** There are five conditions required for a population to stay in Hardy-Weinberg equilibrium:
> - Very large population: No genetic drift can occur.
> - No emigration or immigration: No gene flow can occur.
> - No mutations: No new alleles can be formed in the gene pool.
> - Random mating: No sexual selection can occur.
> - No natural selection: All alleles must be equally advantageous for survival.
>
> The Hardy-Weinberg equation can be used to predict genotype frequencies in a population. The phenotype frequencies must be known, and from these the allele and genotype frequencies can be predicted. If real genotype frequencies do not match the predicted frequencies, the population is not in Hardy-Weinberg equilibrium; it is evolving.
>
> Hardy-Weinberg equilibrium confirms that there are five factors that can lead to evolution: genetic drift, gene flow, mutation, sexual selection, and natural selection. In nature, at least one of these factors is likely to be acting on a population at any given time. Therefore, populations are rarely in equilibrium. In nature, populations evolve.

1. What does the Hardy-Weinberg model show?

_____

2. What conditions are required for a population to stay in Hardy-Weinberg equilibrium?

_____

_____

3. What can be predicted by the Hardy-Weinberg equation?

_____

4. What can be concluded if real population data do not match those predicted by the Hardy-Weinberg equation?

_____

5. Why do real populations rarely reach Hardy-Weinberg equilibrium?

_____

Study Guide

KEY CONCEPT
New species can arise when populations are isolated.

VOCABULARY	
reproductive isolation	geographic isolation
speciation	temporal isolation
behavioral isolation	

MAIN IDEA: The isolation of populations can lead to speciation.

Fill in the term from the box that best completes each statement.

speciation	gene flow	species	gene pools
environments	mutation	mate	genetic drift

1. Two populations are said to be isolated if there is no longer any _____ between them.

2. Over generations, the _____ of isolated populations may become more and more different.

3. Isolated populations may become genetically different as they adapt to new _____ , or through random processes such as mutation and _____ .

4. When members of two isolated populations can no longer _____ successfully, the populations are said to be reproductively isolated.

5. Reproductive isolation is the final step of _____ , which is the rise of new _____ .

6. The experiment illustrated in Figure 11.12 shows how just one _____ can provide enough genetic difference to result in reproductive isolation.

CHAPTER 11
The Evolution of Populations

STUDY GUIDE, CONTINUED

MAIN IDEA: **Populations can become isolated in several ways.**

7. Name the three types of barriers that can isolate populations.

_____

8. In the chart below, take notes about the three ways in which populations can become isolated, leading to reproductive isolation.

Type of Isolation	How It Works	Example
behavioral isolation		
geographic isolation		
temporal isolation		

Vocabulary Check

9. What is speciation?

_____

10. Which type of isolation involves factors of time?

_____

11. Which type of isolation can involve mating or courtship rituals?

_____

12. Which type of isolation can involve physical barriers?

_____

SECTION
11.5

SPECIATION THROUGH ISOLATION
Power Notes

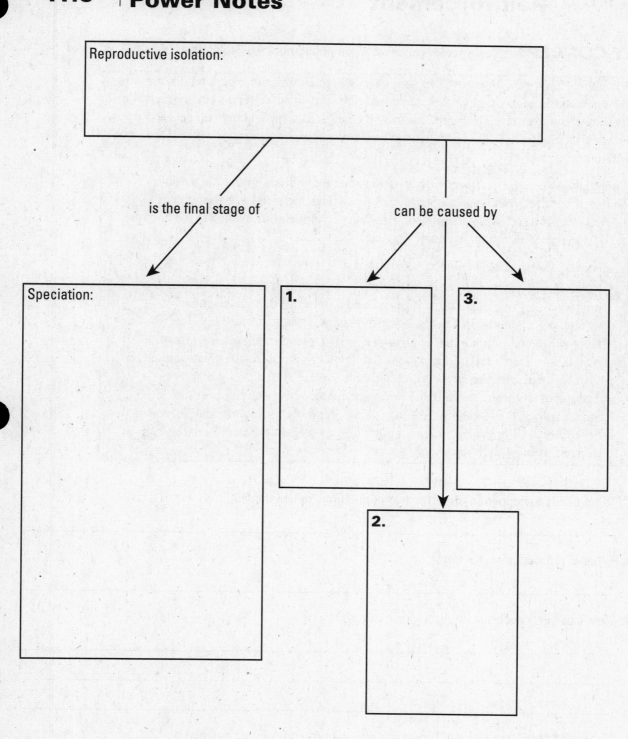

Reproductive isolation:

is the final stage of

can be caused by

Speciation:

1.

3.

2.

Reinforcement

CHAPTER 11
The Evolution of Populations

KEY CONCEPT New species can arise when populations are isolated.

When there is no gene flow between neighboring populations, these populations are said to be isolated from each other. Isolated populations may face different environmental pressures, and over time their gene pools will change. Because there is no gene flow between them, these isolated populations may become more and more genetically different.

If populations become so genetically different that individuals are no longer able to mate successfully with each other, these populations are said to be reproductively isolated. **Reproductive isolation** is the final stage in **speciation,** which is the rise of two or more species from one existing species.

Populations can become isolated in several ways:

- **Behavioral isolation** exists if differences in courtship or mating behaviors prevent individuals of two populations from mating. Behavioral isolation includes differences in courtship dances, courtship songs, and pheromones.
- **Geographic isolation** exists if physical barriers prevent individuals of two populations from mating. Geographic isolation can be caused by rivers, mountains, shifting continents, and even dried lakebeds.
- **Temporal isolation** exists if the timing of reproductive activity prevents individuals of two populations from mating. Temporal isolation includes seasonal differences in life cycles and mating periods, as well as differences in the time of day that most individuals are active.

1. What needs to happen in order for two populations to be isolated?

_____

2. What is reproductive isolation?

_____

3. How can new species arise through isolation?

_____

_____

_____

4. Name and describe three ways in which populations can become isolated.

_____

_____

_____

SECTION 11.6 | PATTERNS IN EVOLUTION
Study Guide

KEY CONCEPT

Evolution occurs in patterns.

VOCABULARY		
convergent evolution	coevolution	punctuated equilibrium
divergent evolution	extinction	adaptive radiation

MAIN IDEA: Evolution through natural selection is not random.

Fill in the Main Idea in the center of the Main Idea Web below. Then take notes based on the phrases in the surrounding boxes.

2. Natural selection has direction:

3. Its effects are cumulative:

1. Main idea:

4. Convergent evolution:

5. Divergent evolution:

MAIN IDEA: Species can shape each other over time.

In the table below, take notes about two ways in which species can coevolve.

Type of Coevolution	How It Works	Example
6. beneficial relationship		
7. evolutionary arms race		

STUDY GUIDE, CONTINUED

MAIN IDEA: Species can become extinct.

In the table below, take notes about background and mass extinctions.

Type of Extinction	Possible Causes	Outcome
8. background extinction		
9. mass extinction		

MAIN IDEA: Speciation often occurs in patterns.

10. The theory of punctuated equilibrium states that relatively brief episodes of

_____ are followed by long periods of little evolutionary

_____ .

11. Adaptive radiation is a process in which one ancestral species diversifies into many

_____ species.

12. Adaptive radiation occurred after the extinction of the dinosaurs, because they left a

wide range of _____ into which mammals could diversify.

Vocabulary Check

13. *Converge* means "to come together" and *diverge* means "to branch out." How do these meanings apply to the terms *convergent* and *divergent evolution*?

_____

_____

14. The prefix *co-* means "together." How does this meaning apply to the term *coevolution*?

_____

15. *Punctuate* means "to interrupt periodically." How does this meaning apply to the term *punctuated equilibrium*?

_____

SECTION
11.6

PATTERNS IN EVOLUTION
Power Notes

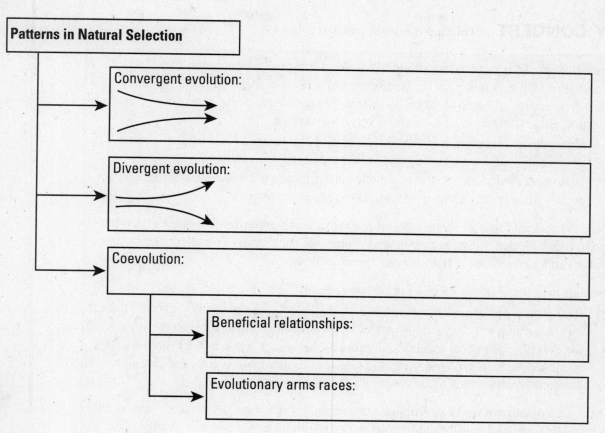

Patterns in Natural Selection

Convergent evolution:

Divergent evolution:

Coevolution:

Beneficial relationships:

Evolutionary arms races:

Extinction:

Background extinction:

Mass extinction:

Patterns in Speciation

Punctuated equilibrium:

Adaptive radiation:

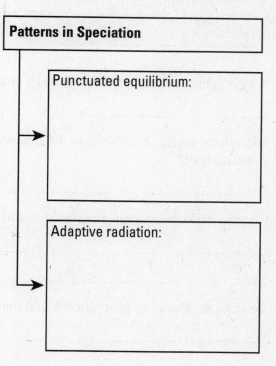

SECTION 11.6 | PATTERNS IN EVOLUTION
Reinforcement

KEY CONCEPT Evolution occurs in patterns.

Natural selection is not random. Natural selection can push a population's traits in a certain direction depending on the environmental pressures. And the resulting changes in allele frequencies add up over time. Two clear trends that can occur as a result of natural selection are convergent evolution and divergent evolution:

- **Convergent evolution** is the evolution toward similar traits in unrelated species. This occurs when unrelated species adapt to similar environments.
- **Divergent evolution** is the evolution toward different traits in related species. This occurs when related species adapt to different environments.

Different species can also shape each other over time. **Coevolution** is a process in which two or more species evolve in response to changes in each other. The relationships that evolve can be beneficial to both species or competitive.

Extinction is the elimination of a species from Earth.

- Background extinctions occur continuously at a low rate and occur at about the same rate as speciation. They can be caused by local changes in an ecosystem.
- Mass extinctions occur much less frequently, but they are much more intense. They occur suddenly in geologic time, due to global catastrophic events, and can destroy hundreds or thousands of species at a time.

The theory of **punctuated equilibrium** states that speciation occurs suddenly and rapidly in geologic time, and is followed by long periods with little evolutionary change. The rapid speciation of one ancestral species into many descendant species is called **adaptive radiation.**

1. Why is natural selection not considered a random event?

_____

2. Two related species become more different over time. What type of evolution is this an example of?

_____

3. Contrast background extinctions and mass extinctions.

_____

_____

4. Describe the theory of punctuated equilibrium.

_____

_____

CHAPTER
11

IDENTIFYING PATTERNS IN DATA
Data Analysis Practice

Identifying patterns in data by studying graphs and charts is important in making future predictions and hypotheses.

Swordtails are small freshwater fish. One section of the tail of the male swordfish is elongated and has a specific color pattern of two black lines running the outside length of the section, with yellow in the middle. Scientists conducted an experiment to determine which component of the color pattern may be most attractive to the female swordtail during mating. The females were exposed to three different stimuli: a normal male swordfish tail, an all-black male swordfish tail, and an all-yellow male swordfish tail. The response of the females to each stimulus was recorded. The graph below shows the results of the research.

GRAPH 1. TYPE OF SWORDFISH TAIL

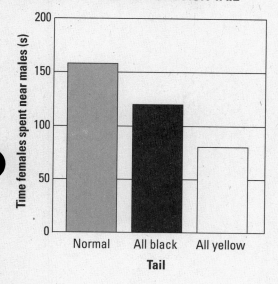

1. **Analyze** What pattern, if any, exists in the data?

_____

_____

_____

_____

2. **Predict** What might happen to a male swordtail with an all-yellow tail during mating season?

_____

_____

Copyright © McDougal Littell/Houghton Mifflin Company.

CHAPTER 11
The Evolution of Populations

CHAPTER
11 | CALCULATING GENE FREQUENCIES
Pre-AP Activity

You have learned in Chapter 11 that the genetic variation of a population is stored in its gene pool, which contains all of the alleles of every individual in that population. Each allele exists at a certain frequency in the population. This reflects how common that allele is in the current population under its current environmental circumstances. The relative frequency of the individual alleles for a given trait may shift if changes in environmental conditions favor a different phenotype.

MENDELIAN INHERITANCE: A BRIEF REVIEW

Before we begin calculating gene frequencies, let's review some of the ground rules of genetic inheritance and make some assumptions about our theoretical populations. First, assume that all of our populations are diploid—each individual carries two alleles for each gene. Therefore, the total number of alleles in a population is two times the number of population members: if the population has 200 individuals, then the gene pool has 400 alleles.

Second, gene frequencies are expressed mathematically from 0 to 1. A gene frequency of 1 means that everyone in the population carries that allele; such an allele is said to be fixed in the population. An allele frequency of 0 means that no one carries the allele; it is therefore locally extinct. The total of allele frequencies for a particular gene in a population will always add up to 1. For a population in which the frequency of allele $A = 0.73$, the frequency of allele a will equal $1 - 0.73$, or 0.27.

Lastly, assume that the traits examined in this activity follow Mendelian autosomal dominant-recessive inheritance. Individuals who are homozygous dominant carry two dominant alleles (AA), homozygous recessives carry two recessive alleles (aa), and heterozygotes carry one of each allele (Aa).

USING GENE COUNTS

The simplest way to calculate an allele's frequency is to count the number of times an allele occurs in the gene pool, and divide this by the total number of alleles for that gene in the gene pool. The frequency of the dominant allele will equal two times the number of homozygous dominant individuals plus the number of heterozygotes; the frequency of the recessive allele will equal two times the number of recessive individuals plus the number of heterozygotes.

$$f(A) = 2AA + Aa$$
$$f(a) = 2aa + Aa$$

EXAMPLE

Coat length in cats is a Mendelian trait in which short hair (S) is dominant to long hair (s). In a hypothetical population of 978 stray cats living in a city park, 372 are SS, 534 are Ss, and 72 are ss. To find the frequency of the short-hair and long-hair alleles, calculate the total number of alleles, and then the proportion of each.

CHAPTER 11
The Evolution of Populations

1. If there are 978 cats, then the gene pool has 2 x 978 alleles for hair length = **1956 alleles**

2. $f(S) = (2\,SS + Ss)$ / total alleles
   $[(2 \times 372) + 534] / 1956 = (744 + 534) / 1956 = 0.65$
   $f(S) = 0.65$

3. $f(s) = (2\,ss + Ss)$ / total alleles
   $[(2 \times 72) + 534] / 1956 = (144 + 534) / 1956$
   $f(s) = 0.35$

4. Confirmation:
   $f(S) + f(s) = 1$
   $0.65 + 0.35 = 1$

HOW GENE FREQUENCIES ARE USED

By calculating allele frequencies for a given gene, we can get an idea of how common or rare a particular allele or phenotype is in a population. In our hypothetical stray cat population, we would expect the ratio of short-haired to long-haired cats to be 3:1, but it is closer to 2:1. This may suggest that in this particular population there is a selective advantage to long hair. Or it could suggest that long-haired cats are mating with each other more frequently than they are with short-haired cats, and that their reproductive success is greater. If the frequency of the long-hair allele were very low, we might think that long-hair was disadvantageous in addition to being genetically recessive.

To learn more about a trait in a population and how the environment and other factors may be affecting allele frequencies, scientists have to track allele frequencies over a period of generations. Changes in allele frequencies over time may indicate changes in environmental circumstances, shifts in behaviors, the relative fitness of each allele, and more.

Answer the following questions on a separate sheet of paper.

1. Two years after the above frequencies were calculated, a biologist reexamined the cat population and counted 153 short-haired homozygotes, 568 short-haired heterozygotes, and 397 long-haired cats. What are the frequencies of each allele now? Be sure to show your work.

2. Did the gene frequencies change? If so, how? Why might this have occurred?

3. What other way could you calculate the frequency of the long-hair allele in the question and example above?

4. Imagine that an analysis of the same stray cat population ten years later showed that the long-haired cats had all but disappeared. What could this mean for the genetic diversity of this population? And what might this mean for the future of this population? Explain.

CHAPTER 11
The Evolution of Populations

CHAPTER 11

EVOLUTIONARY ADVANTAGES OF SEXUAL
REPRODUCTION

Pre-AP Activity

You have learned in Chapter 11 that some organisms reproduce asexually while others do so sexually. At a cursory glance, sexual reproduction seems to have fewer survival benefits: it takes time and effort to find a partner, and you can only pass on half your genes. In this activity you will learn about sexual reproduction's advantages.

POPULATION GROWTH

If you had four asexual organisms that produced two offspring each per reproductive cycle, you'd get eight new offspring in a new generation. If you had four sexually reproducing organisms—two males and two females—that paired up to produce two offspring per reproductive cycle per couple, you would get four offspring. That's because the sexual organisms have to pair up. In this scenario, the asexual group "wins"—it grows twice as fast as the sexual reproducing group. However, this scenario isn't very realistic, because it assumes that reproductive rates are the same, and it does not account for all of the challenges that organisms face once they are born, such as predation and disease. To understand the advantage of sexual reproduction, we have to take a closer look at what sexual reproduction really means.

GENETIC INFORMATION

Fitness is defined as reproductive success—how many of your genes end up in the next generation. It follows, then, that we could compare the percentage of an individual's genes passed on to offspring through asexual reproduction versus the percentage passed on through sexual reproduction.

Let's assume that a sexual organism and an asexual organism each have a genome containing 10 genes. An asexual organism will transmit all 10 genes to each of its offspring. In contrast, the sexually produced offspring will only inherit half of each parent's genes. This is because each diploid parent will produce a haploid gamete containing half of that parent's genes. When the male gamete fuses with the female gamete, it will form an offspring with a full set of genes—half of its mother's genes and half of its father's.

So far, asexual reproduction is winning.

DISEASE AND THE RED QUEEN

In the 1970s, a group of scientists at the University of Michigan devised a computer simulation to model reproduction and disease. The model began with a hypothetical population of 200 individuals—some sexual and others asexual. Death was introduced randomly. The simulation ran for a given period of time, during which the two groups reproduced. As was expected, the asexual population always had more individuals at the end of the simulation.

The scientists then introduced a hypothetical group of parasites and reran the simulation. This time, the sexual population won. As the simulations were repeated, the sexual population won most of the time.

The explanation for the results of the simulation became the Red Queen hypothesis, an idea whose name derives from the character in *Alice's Adventures in Wonderland* who must keep running as fast as she can just to stay in place. The Red Queen concept describes the reciprocal "arms race" that exists between parasites and their victims. When a parasite

CHAPTER 11
The Evolution of Populations

evolves new proteins on its surface, the host must evolve reciprocal receptors to resist infection. The parasite in turn then evolves more new proteins, which are met by newly evolved receptors in the host. Novel variations arise in traits such as cell receptors either through mutation, which is rare, or recombination. And it is recombination, or rather, the ability to undergo it, that gives sexual reproduction its greatest advantage.

1. In the first two scenarios described on the previous page, why did asexual reproduction "win" over sexual reproduction? What happened in the computer simulation that shifted the advantage to sexual reproduction?

_____

_____

_____

_____

_____

_____

_____

2. What exactly is the Red Queen hypothesis? Explain its relevance in this exercise.

_____

_____

_____

_____

_____

_____

_____

_____

CHAPTER 11

THE EVOLUTION OF POPULATIONS
Vocabulary Practice

gene pool	genetic drift	geographic isolation
allele frequency	bottleneck effect	temporal isolation
normal distribution	founder effect	convergent evolution
microevolution	sexual selection	divergent evolution
directional selection	Hardy-Weinberg equilibrium	coevolution
stabilizing selection	reproductive isolation	extinction
disruptive selection	speciation	punctuated equilibrium
gene flow	behavioral isolation	adaptive radiation

A. Who Am I? Choose among these terms to answer the riddles below:

behavioral isolation	geographic isolation	temporal isolation
Hardy-Weinberg equilibrium	normal distribution	punctuated equilibrium

1. I separate populations with factors of time, such as when one population reproduces in the spring and another reproduces in the summer. _____

2. I look like a bell-shaped curve, having the highest frequency in the middle. _____

3. I separate populations with physical barriers so that members of each population no longer have contact with each other. _____

4. I occur when there are no changes in allele frequencies for a certain trait from generation to generation; I rarely occur in real populations. _____

5. I am a pattern of evolution that is seen in the fossil record; I consist of short periods with lots of evolutionary activity, followed by long periods with much less evolutionary activity. _____

6. I separate populations with different courtship or mating rituals. _____

VOCABULARY PRACTICE, CONTINUED

B. Word Origins Circle the Greek and Latin word parts in each vocabulary term. Then use the Greek and Latin meanings to construct a very basic definition of the vocabulary word.

co-	=	together
converge	=	to come together from different directions
diverge	=	to go in different directions from a common point
micro-	=	small

WORD	DEFINITION
1. coevolution	
2. convergent evolution	
3. divergent evolution	
4. microevolution	

C. Choose the Correct Word In each set of questions, choose the word from the word box that best fits each statement.

normal distribution	stabilizing selection
directional selection	disruptive selection

1. Occurs when natural selection selects for individuals with the intermediate phenotype   _____

2. Occurs when natural selection is not acting on a population for a certain trait   _____

3. Occurs when natural selection selects for individuals with one extreme phenotype   _____

4. Occurs when natural selection selects for individuals with both extreme phenotypes   _____

VOCABULARY PRACTICE, CONTINUED

reproductive isolation	geographic isolation
behavioral isolation	temporal isolation

5. Species from two populations are separated by physical barriers

_____

6. Species from two populations can no longer mate successfully, for any reason

_____

7. Species from two populations are separated due to differences in courtship or mating rituals

_____

8. Species from two populations are separated due to differences in the timing of their reproduction

_____

microevolution	convergent evolution
coevolution	divergent evolution

9. Process in which two species evolve in response to changes in each other, over many generations

_____

10. Process in which unrelated species evolve similar traits while adapting to similar environments

_____

11. Process in which closely related species become more and more different as they adapt to different environments

_____

12. Process which can occur over a few generations, in which a population's allele frequencies change in any way

_____

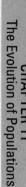

CHAPTER 11
The Evolution of Populations

D. Do-It Yourself Matching In a random order, write short definitions for each term on the blank lines to the right. Then give your paper to a classmate who should write the number of the term next to the correct definition.

1. adaptive radiation   _____   _____

2. gene pool   _____   _____

3. directional selection   _____   _____

4. stabilizing selection   _____   _____

5. disruptive selection   _____   _____

6. speciation   _____   _____

E. Analogies Read each analogy. Decide which term is most like it.

allele frequency	gene pool	normal distribution
extinction	genetic drift	punctuated equilibrium
gene flow	geographic isolation	

1. Long, flat surfaces interrupted by short, steep steps

_____

2. Including only two people in a survey of a large community, and not getting representative results

_____

3. Medium clothing sizes being the most common in a department store

_____

4. A radio station that goes off the air

_____

5. Many colleges sharing and exchanging research ideas with each other

_____

6. How often a certain letter-number combination is called during bingo

_____

7. A phone book that contains all of the phone numbers of everyone in a city

_____

8. Sound-proof glass that prevents people from hearing each other

_____

| THE FOSSIL RECORD
Study Guide

KEY CONCEPT
Fossils are a record of life that existed in the past.

VOCABULARY	
relative dating	isotope
radiometric dating	half-life

MAIN IDEA: **Fossils can form in several ways.**

In the spaces provided, write either the type of fossil being described or a brief description of how the fossil type is formed.

Type of Fossil	Description of Fossil Formation
1.	Organism trapped in tree resin that hardens after being buried.
2.	An impression is left in sediment, and minerals fill the impression in, recreating the original shape of the organism.
3. Trace fossil	
4. Permineralized fossil	
5.	Organism becomes encased in materials such as ice or volcanic ash, or immersed in a bog.

CHAPTER 12
The History of Life

STUDY GUIDE, CONTINUED

Use Figure 12.2 to fill in a sequence diagram that describes the process of permineralization.

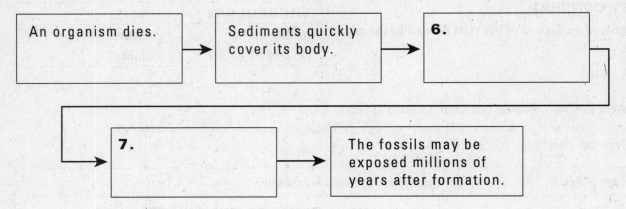

MAIN IDEA: Radiometric dating provides an accurate estimate of a fossil's age.

8. What is the main purpose of both relative dating and radiometric dating?

_____

9. What is the main *difference* between relative dating and radiometric dating?

_____

10. How is the radioactive decay of an element used to determine the age of a rock layer?

_____

_____

11. Look at Figure 12.4. After two half-lives, what percentage of carbon-14 remains in a sample?

_____

Vocabulary Check

relative dating	radiometric dating	isotope	half-life

_____ **12.** Measures the actual age of a fossil

_____ **13.** Most elements have several of these

_____ **14.** Measure of the release of radiation

_____ **15.** Infers order in which groups of organisms existed

SECTION
12.1 | THE FOSSIL RECORD
Power Notes

```
                          ┌─────────────────────┐
                          │  Types of Fossils   │
                          └─────────────────────┘
```

Permineralization:	Natural casts:	Trace fossils:	Preserved remains:

Relative dating:	Radiometric dating:

Isotopes: _____

_____

_____

Shade in the neutrons below.

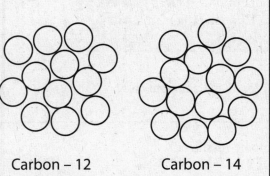

Carbon – 12
___ Protons
___ Neutrons

Carbon – 14
___ Protons
___ Neutrons

Half-life: _____

_____

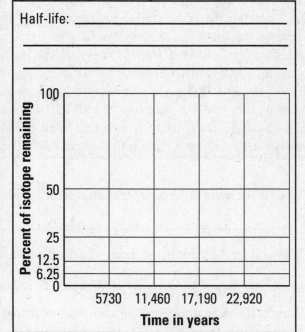

CHAPTER 12
The History of Life

SECTION 12.1

THE FOSSIL RECORD
Reinforcement

CHAPTER 12
The History of Life

KEY CONCEPT   Fossils are a record of life that existed in the past.

Fossils can form in several different ways:

- Permineralization occurs when water surrounds a hard structure such as bone and the minerals from the water are deposited around the structure. Eventually, the minerals can replace the structure itself, making it rocklike.
- Natural casts are made when flowing water removes all of the tissue from the decaying organism, leaving just an impression, or mold, of the organism's shape. Minerals fill in the mold, recreating the original shape of the organism.
- Trace fossils give a clue of how an organism behaved in its environment. Rather than the organism itself, a trace fossil can be a nest, a burrow, or an imprint.
- Amber-preserved fossils are formed when small organisms such as insects become trapped in tree resin. Eventually, the tree is buried and the resin hardens into amber, allowing the organism to be seen inside.
- Preserved remains occur when an organism becomes surrounded by a material that preserves it, such as ice, volcanic ash, or the organic matter of a bog.

Because such specific conditions must be present in order for fossilization to occur, only a small percentage of living things that ever existed become fossils. Most remains of organisms decompose or are destroyed before they could be preserved. Even after something becomes fossilized, natural events such as earthquakes and the recycling of rock into magma can destroy fossils that took thousands of years to form.

The age of a fossil or rock can be estimated by **relative dating**, in which the fossil location is compared to rock layers of known age. Fossil age can also be measured by **radiometric** dating, which uses radioactive isotopes to determine a fossil's age. **Isotopes** are forms of an element that have the same number of protons but a different number of neutrons. Most elements have several isotopes. Some isotopes have unstable nuclei and undergo radioactive decay. As an isotope decays, it can transform into a different element. The decay rate of many radioactive isotopes has been measured and is known as the isotope's half-life. A **half-life** is the amount of time it takes for half of the isotope in a sample to decay into a different element. Through radiometric dating, scientists have estimated that Earth is about 4.5 billion years old.

1. What is the main difference between a permineralized fossil and a natural cast?

_____

2. Why is it unlikely for the remains of a dead organism to be fossilized?

_____

3. What is the main difference between relative dating and radiometric dating?

_____

SECTION
12.2 | THE GEOLOGIC TIME SCALE
Study Guide

KEY CONCEPT
The geologic time scale divides Earth's history based on major past events.

VOCABULARY		
index fossil	era	epoch
geologic time scale	period	

MAIN IDEA: Index fossils are another tool to determine the age of rock layers.

1. How are index fossils used to determine the age of fossils or rock layers?

_____

2. What four characteristics are best for an index fossil to have?

_____

MAIN IDEA: The geologic time scale organizes Earth's history.
Look at Figure 12.6 to fill in the following classification tree.

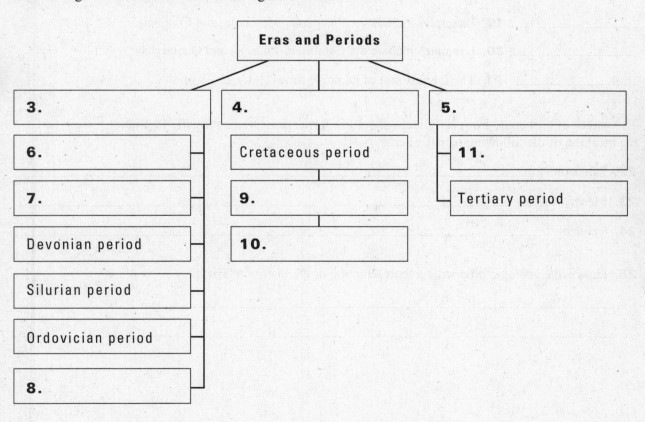

Eras and Periods

3.   4.   5.

6.   Cretaceous period   11.

7.   9.   Tertiary period

Devonian period   10.

Silurian period

Ordovician period

8.

CHAPTER 12
The History of Life

Vocabulary Check

era	period	epoch

Fill in the blanks below using the terms in the box. You may use some terms more than others.

_____ **12.** The smallest unit of geologic time

_____ **13.** Associated with rock systems

_____ **14.** Consists of two or more periods

_____ **15.** Lasts tens to hundreds of millions of years

_____ **16.** Lasts several million years

_____ **17.** Lasts tens of millions of years

_____ **18.** Most commonly used units of geologic time

_____ **19.** Examples include the Paleozoic, Mesozoic, and Cenozoic

_____ **20.** Examples include the Cambrian, Jurassic, and Quaternary

_____ **21.** The longest unit of geologic time

The names of eras come from early ideas about life forms preserved as fossils. Provide the meaning of the following names of eras:

22. Paleozoic _____

23. Mesozoic _____

24. Cenozoic _____

25. How is the geologic time scale a representation of the history of Earth?

_____

_____

SECTION 12.2

THE GEOLOGIC TIME SCALE
Power Notes

Definition:	Characteristics:
Example:	Nonexample:

Index Fossil

Geologic Time Scale:

Eras:

Periods:

Epochs:

1. Era:

Description:

2. Era:

Description:

3. Era:

Description:

CHAPTER 12
The History of Life

THE GEOLOGIC TIME SCALE
Reinforcement

KEY CONCEPT The geologic time scale divides Earth's history based on major past events.

Index fossils can be used along with radiometric dating to determine the age of a fossil or rock. **Index fossils** are fossils of organisms that existed only during specific spans of time over large regions on Earth. The best index fossils are plentiful, easy to recognize, found throughout the world, and only lived for a relatively short time. The shorter the life span was of a species used as an index fossil, the more precisely the layer of rock containing that index fossil can be dated. Index fossils are a tool for relative dating of rock layers.

The **geologic time scale** organizes the Earth's major geologic and biological events into a representation of Earth's history. The time scale is divided into three basic units of time.

- **Eras** are made up of two or more periods and last tens to hundreds of millions of years.
- **Periods** are the most commonly used units of time on the geologic time scale. They last tens of millions of years.
- **Epochs** are the smallest units of geologic time and last several million years.

The names of the eras—*Paleozoic*, *Mesozoic*, and *Cenozoic*—came from early ideas about the life forms that lived during those times. *Paleozoic* means "ancient life," *Mesozoic* means "middle life," and *Cenozoic* means "recent life." Periods are often named based on a particular type of rock system formed during that time interval. The boundaries between many of the geologic periods are defined by mass extinction events.

1. Why are the best index fossils from species that only existed for a short period of time?

_____

_____

2. The geologic time scale was created by scientists. What is its purpose?

_____

_____

3. Based upon the meaning of the words, what era do we live in?

_____

_____

4. Many geologic periods were defined by events that made a natural boundary to the period. Oftentimes, what were these events?

_____

12.3 | ORIGIN OF LIFE
Study Guide

KEY CONCEPT
The origin of life on Earth remains a puzzle.

VOCABULARY	
nebula	ribozyme

MAIN IDEA: **Earth was very different billions of years ago.**

1. Most scientists agree on two points about Earth's origins. What are they?

_____

_____

_____

Fill in the Main Idea Web with the descriptions of early Earth.

Heat released by:
2._____
and
3._____

Atmosphere made of:
4._____
Absent in atmosphere:
5._____

Earth was very different billions of years ago.

Eon name:
6._____

Energy provided by:
7._____
and
8._____

CHAPTER 12
The History of Life

STUDY GUIDE, CONTINUED

MAIN IDEA: Several sets of hypotheses propose how life began on Earth.

In the column on the left labeled "hypothesis," write the hypothesis from the readings about how life began on Earth. In the column labeled "proof," list the evidence that supports the hypothesis.

Hypothesis	Proof
I. ORGANIC MOLECULE HYPOTHESES	
9.	Demonstrated organic compounds could be made by passing electrical current (to simulate lightning) through a closed system that held a mixture of gases (to simulate the early atmosphere).
10. Meteorite hypothesis	
II. EARLY CELL STRUCTURE HYPOTHESES	
11.	Simulated in the lab, making a chimney structure with compartments that could have acted as the first cell membranes.
12. Lipid membrane hypothesis	
III. RNA AS EARLY GENETIC MATERIAL	
13. RNA world hypothesis	

Vocabulary Check

_____ **14.** A cloud of gas and dust in space

_____ **15.** An RNA molecule that can catalyze specific chemical reactions

SECTION
12.3 | ORIGIN OF LIFE
Power Notes

Main Idea: The Origin of Life	Detail Notes:
I. Organic molecule hypotheses	**1.** Miller-Urey experiment: **2.** Meteorite hypothesis:
II. Early cell structure hypotheses	**1.** Iron-sulfide bubbles hypothesis: **2.** Lipid membrane hypothesis:
III. RNA as early genetic material	**1.** Ribozymes:

CHAPTER 12
The History of Life

SECTION 12.3 | ORIGIN OF LIFE
Reinforcement

KEY CONCEPT   The origin of life on Earth remains a puzzle.

Details of Earth's beginnings are still unknown, although most scientists agree that (1) Earth is billions of years old, and (2) the conditions of early Earth were very different from those of today. The most widely accepted hypothesis of Earth's origins proposes that the solar system was formed by a condensing **nebula**, a cloud of gas and dust in space. This hypothesis is supported by computer models and observations made with the Hubble Space Telescope.

There are several sets of hypotheses to explain how life began on Earth. Organic molecule hypotheses consider how the very first life-supporting molecules arose on Earth. One organic molecule hypothesis was proposed as a result of a famous experiment. Stanley Miller and Harold Urey modeled conditions of early Earth in the laboratory and found that organic molecules can be made from a mixture of gases (representing the atmosphere) and an electrical current (representing lightning). The Miller-Urey hypothesis suggests that organic molecules formed spontaneously on early Earth. Another organic molecule hypothesis, known as the meteorite hypothesis, proposes that the first organic molecules on Earth arrived from outer space. A meteorite that fell to Earth in 1969 was found to have more than 90 amino acids, and was the basis for this hypothesis.

Early cell structure hypotheses consider how the first cells may have formed. Examples include the iron-sulfide bubbles hypothesis, which proposes that chimneylike structures on the ocean floor contain compartments that may have acted as the first cells. Laboratory experiments modeled this process, creating similar structures with elements such as iron, sodium, and sulfur. Another early cell structure hypothesis is the lipid membrane hypothesis. The lipid membrane hypothesis is based on the observation that lipid, or fat, molecules spontaneously form spheres that resemble cells. Perhaps they acted as the first cell membranes.

One hypothesis considers early genetic material. The discovery of **ribozymes**, RNA molecules that can catalyze specific reactions, led to the hypothesis that perhaps RNA came before DNA on early Earth.

1. What are two types of evidence that support the hypothesis that Earth and the rest of the solar system was formed by a condensing nebula?

   _____

2. How did the Miller-Urey experiment model conditions of early Earth?

   _____

CHAPTER 12
The History of Life

SECTION
12.4 | EARLY SINGLE-CELLED ORGANISMS
Study Guide

KEY CONCEPT
Single-celled organisms existed 3.8 billion years ago.

VOCABULARY	
cyanobacteria	endosymbiosis

MAIN IDEA: Microbes have changed the physical and chemical composition of Earth.

1. What are two ways that early single-celled organisms changed Earth's surface?

_____

2. What have scientists inferred from fossil stromatolites?

_____

MAIN IDEA: Eukaryotic cells may have evolved through endosymbiosis.
Fill in the blanks with the correct terms.

3. Although prokaryotes existed as long as 3.5 billion years ago, _____ arose about 1.5 billion years ago.

4. Eukaryotes have a _____ and membrane-bound organelles.

5. Eukaryotes are _____ , which means they need oxygen to survive.

6. While the first eukaryotes were made of only one _____ , later eukaryotes were made of many.

Use the sequence diagram below to summarize the theory of endosymbiosis.

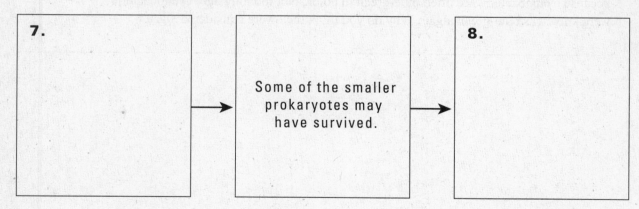

| 7. | | Some of the smaller prokaryotes may have survived. | | 8. |

CHAPTER 12
The History of Life

9. Describe the role that cyanobacteria play in the theory of endosymbiosis.

_____

_____

_____

MAIN IDEA: **The evolution of sexual reproduction led to increased diversity.**

10. What is the main advantage of asexual reproduction?

_____

11. Sexual reproduction increases genetic variation in a population. Why might this be beneficial to the population?

_____

Vocabulary Check

12. Bacteria that can carry out photosynthesis are called _____ .

13. The mutually beneficial relationship in which one organism lives within the body of

another is called _____ .

14. The term *endosymbiosis* can be broken down into parts. *Endo-* means "within." What is another term you have heard that starts with *endo-*?

_____

15. The term *cyanobacteria* can be broken down into parts. *Cyan-* means "greenish blue," because cyanobacteria are often blue-green in color. Not too long ago, cyanobacteria were known as blue-green algae. Why do you think they were considered algae?

_____

SECTION
12.4 | EARLY SINGLE-CELLED ORGANISMS
Power Notes

Cyanobacteria: _____

_____

_____

_____

changed Earth by

1.

2.

Endosymbiosis: _____

_____

_____

1. _____

_____

Sketch:

2. _____

_____

Sketch:

3. _____

_____

Sketch:

CHAPTER 12
The History of Life

CHAPTER 12
The History of Life

SECTION
12.4 | EARLY SINGLE-CELLED ORGANISMS
Reinforcement

KEY CONCEPT Single-celled organisms existed 3.8 billion years ago.

The first organisms on Earth were most likely prokaryotes, such as bacteria, that didn't need oxygen to survive. Once life began to thrive, Earth began to change. These single-celled organisms eventually began depositing minerals on the Earth's surface and adding oxygen to the atmosphere as a by-product of photosynthesis. Scientists have found evidence, through fossils, that photosynthetic life evolved more than 3.5 billion years ago. These fossils are remains of a group of marine **cyanobacteria**, which are bacteria that can carry out photosynthesis. Some cyanobacteria live in colonies and form stromatolites—domed, rocky structures made of layers of cyanobacteria and sediment. Communities of photosynthesizing cyanobacteria in stromatolites raised the oxygen levels in the atmosphere and ocean, which allowed the evolution of aerobic life forms, which need oxygen to live.

Endosymbiosis is a relationship in which one organism lives within the body of another and both benefit from the relationship. The theory of endosymbiosis proposes that the first eukaryotic cells arose from a large prokaryote engulfing a smaller prokaryote. Over many generations, the smaller prokaryote evolved as mitochondria or, if they were photosynthetic, chloroplasts. Unlike a prokaryote, a eukaryote has a nucleus and other membrane-bound organelles.

The fossil record shows that eukaryotic organisms had evolved by 1.5 billion years ago. Eukaryotic organisms were all aerobic. While the first eukaryotes were made of only one cell, later eukaryotes were multicellular—made of many cells.

1. Why is it reasonable to assume that the earliest life on Earth was anaerobic, not needing oxygen to survive?

_____

2. How are cyanobacteria different from most bacteria?

_____

3. The theory of endosymbiosis describes the probable evolution of what type of cell?

_____

4. Mitochondria and chloroplasts both have their own DNA and ribosomes. How does this information support the theory of endosymbiosis?

_____

_____

_____

SECTION
12.5
RADIATION OF MULTICELLULAR LIFE
Study Guide

KEY CONCEPT
Multicellular life evolved in distinct phases.

VOCABULARY	
Paleozoic	Mesozoic
Cambrian explosion	Cenozoic

MAIN IDEA: Life moved onto land during the Paleozoic era.

Fill in a Main Idea and Supporting Information Diagram describing the Paleozoic era.

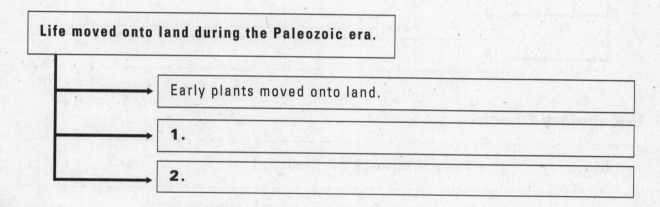

Life moved onto land during the Paleozoic era.

Early plants moved onto land.

1.

2.

MAIN IDEA: Reptiles radiated during the Mesozoic era.

Fill in a Main Idea and Supporting Information Diagram describing the Mesozoic era.

Reptiles radiated during the Mesozoic era.

3.

4.

5.

CHAPTER 12
The History of Life

MAIN IDEA: **Mammals radiated during the Cenozoic era.**

Fill in a Main Idea and Supporting Information Diagram describing the Cenozoic era.

6.

7.

8.

9.

Vocabulary Check

Paleozoic	Cambrian explosion	Mesozoic	Cenozoic

_____ **10.** Divided into the Triassic, Jurassic, and Cretaceous periods

_____ **11.** Ended with a mass extinction with more than 90 percent of all marine life extinct

_____ **12.** Earliest part of Paleozoic era

_____ **13.** Primates evolved during this era

_____ **14.** Trilobites were abundant then

_____ **15.** Rise of the first marsupial mammals

_____ **16.** Divided into Tertiary and Quarternary periods

_____ **17.** Life moved onto land

_____ **18.** Includes the Carboniferous period

_____ **19.** Dinosaurs roamed the earth

_____ **20.** Continues today

CHAPTER 12
The History of Life

Multicellular Life Evolved in Distinct Phases.

Paleozoic

   Years:

   Major events:

Cambrian explosion:

Mesozoic

   Years:

   Known as:

   Major events:

Cenozoic

   Years:

   Major events:

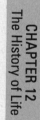

CHAPTER 12
The History of Life

SECTION 12.5 | RADIATION OF MULTICELLULAR LIFE
Reinforcement

KEY CONCEPT Multicellular life evolved in distinct phases.

The trend toward multicellular, or many-celled, organisms was one of the most important transitions in the history of life. It may have been an advantage for early one-celled organisms to increase in size by becoming multicellular. Cells that cooperated could compete more effectively for energy, through processes such as cooperative feeding. At some point, increased dependence on neighboring cells would have led the cells to function as a colony, and eventually as a single, multicellular organism. Multicellular life on Earth evolved in distinct phases.

- Multicellular organisms first appeared during the **Paleozoic** era, which began 544 million years ago. Members of every major animal group evolved within only a few million years. The earliest part of the Paleozoic era is the Cambrian period, also known as the **Cambrian explosion.** During the Cambrian explosion, a huge diversity of animal species evolved. At the start of the Paleozoic era, all life was found in the ocean. The middle of the Paleozoic era was a time of great diversity as life moved onto land, and four-legged vertebrates such as amphibians became common. The Paleozoic era ended 248 million years ago with a mass extinction in which more than 90 percent of marine animals and 70 percent of land animal species of that time became extinct.

- During the **Mesozoic** era—which began 248 million years ago—dinosaurs, flowering plants, and birds inhabited Earth. The Mesozoic era is divided into three periods: the Triassic, the Jurassic, and the Cretaceous periods. The first mammals arose during the Triassic period, and the Cretaceous period was the peak in dinosaur diversity. This period ended 65 million years ago with the most famous of the mass extinctions, causing the dinosaurs to become extinct.

- During the **Cenozoic** era—which began 65 million years ago—mammals diversified, as did birds, fishes, and flowering plants. The Cenozoic era is divided into two periods, the Tertiary and the Quaternary periods. Modern humans, *Homo sapiens*, did not appear until 100,000 years ago, well into the Quaternary period, which continues today.

1. Why is the Cambrian period also known as the Cambrian explosion?

_____

2. What group of animals arose during the Mesozoic era but diversified in the Cenozoic era?

_____

3. What type of reptile did not survive the mass extinction event at the end of the Mesozoic era?

_____

SECTION
12.6 | PRIMATE EVOLUTION
Study Guide

KEY CONCEPT
Humans appeared late in Earth's history.

VOCABULARY	
primate	hominid
prosimian	bipedal
anthropoid	

MAIN IDEA: Humans share a common ancestor with other primates.
Use Figure 12.18 to help you fill in the concept map below with the correct primate group.

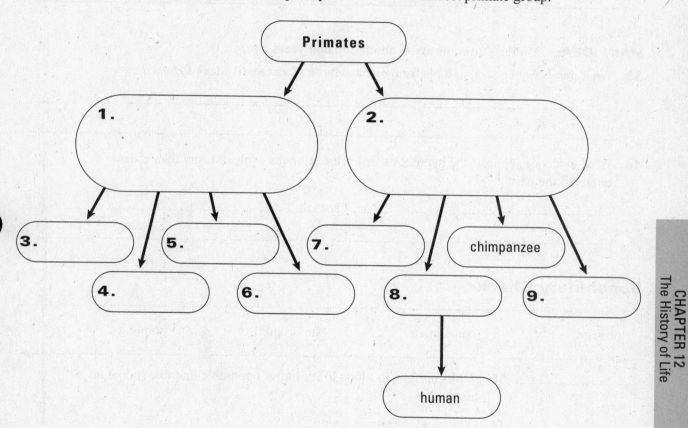

CHAPTER 12
The History of Life

STUDY GUIDE, CONTINUED

MAIN IDEA: There are many fossil of extinct hominids.

10. What are the two groups that most hominid species are classified into?

_____

11. What early hominid was known as "handy man"?

_____

12. What early hominid group may have existed alongside modern humans?

_____

MAIN IDEA: Modern humans arose about 200,000 years ago.

13. What trends can be seen in tools from older to more recent fossil sites of *Homo*?

_____

_____

14. What evidence supports the hypothesis that primate brains evolved faster than rodent brains in the past?

_____

_____

Vocabulary Check

primate	prosimian	anthropoid	hominid

_____ **15.** Walks upright, has long lower limbs, opposable thumbs, and large brains

_____ **16.** Oldest living primate group

_____ **17.** Name means humanlike primate

_____ **18.** Has flexible hands and feet, eyes that face forward, and large brains

_____ **19.** Small primate that is active at night

_____ **20.** Includes all species in human lineage, both modern and extinct

_____ **21.** Examples include lemurs, lorises, and tarsiers

_____ **22.** Divided into New World monkeys, Old World monkeys, and hominoids

SECTION
12.6 | PRIMATE EVOLUTION
Power Notes

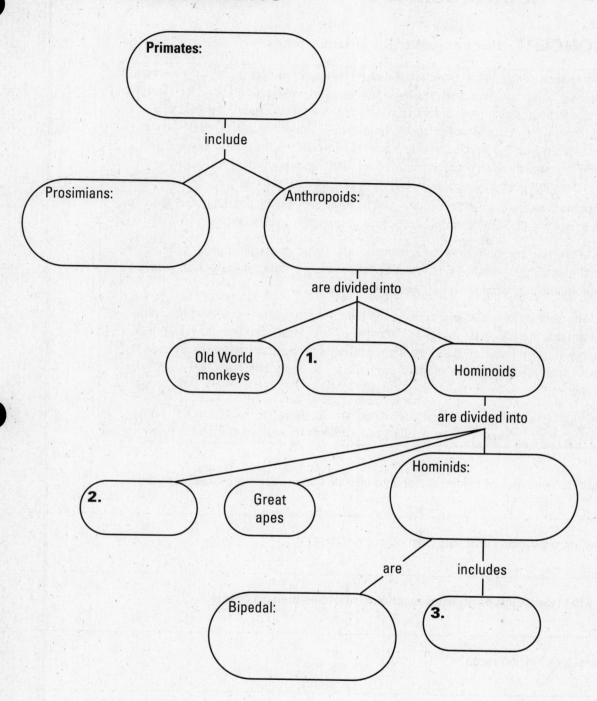

Primates:

include

Prosimians: Anthropoids:

are divided into

Old World monkeys   1.   Hominoids

are divided into

2.   Great apes   Hominids:

are   includes

Bipedal: 3.

CHAPTER 12
The History of Life

PRIMATE EVOLUTION
Reinforcement

KEY CONCEPT Humans appeared late in Earth's history.

Humans share a common ancestor with other primates. **Primates** include all mammals with flexible hands and feet, forward-looking eyes, and enlarged brains relative to their body size. Primates also have arms that can rotate in a circle around their shoulder joint, and many primates have opposable thumbs that can move against their fingers. Besides sharing similar physical traits, primates share strong molecular similarities. Like other groups of related organisms, the relationship among the primate groups forms a many-branched evolutionary tree.

- **Prosimians** are the oldest primate group. They are mostly small animals that are active at night. Some examples are lemurs, lorises, and tarsiers.

- **Anthropoid** means "humanlike primate," and is the term used for the group that includes all the primates that are not prosimians, including monkeys, gibbons, orangutans, chimpanzees, and gorillas.

- **Hominids** include all the species in the human lineage, both modern and extinct. Hominids are **bipedal**—they walk upright on two legs, have long lower limbs, opposable thumbs, and relatively large brains. There are many fossils of extinct hominids. *Homo sapiens,* modern humans, are the only hominids that are alive today.

Fossil evidence shows that the first appearance of *Homo sapiens* dates back to about 200,000 years ago. Many of their features are different than those of humans today.

1. What are two types of evidence that demonstrate that primates are closely related?

_____

2. How are prosimians different from other primates?

_____

3. To what two groups of primates mentioned above do humans belong?

_____

4. What does bipedal mean?

_____

5. What type of evidence indicates *Homo sapiens* have existed for about 200,000 years?

_____

CHAPTER 12

DETERMINING AXIS SCALES
Data Analysis Practice

Choosing appropriate intervals with which to label the axes of a graph is an important part of accurately representing data collected from an experiment.

Researchers collected data on the number of recorded extinctions over the last 400 years. The results of their research are shown in the table below.

Extinctions Per Year	
Year	Number of Recorded Extinctions
1600	0
1650	5
1700	20
1750	13
1800	21
1850	25
1900	116
1950	140
2000	61

1. **Synthesize** Calculate intervals to be used for the scale of the x-axis and y-axis and construct a line graph to display the data.

CHAPTER 12
The History of Life

_____

2. Evaluate Why would you *not* want to have the x-axis in intervals of 10 for this graph?

_____

_____

_____

_____

| GEOLOGIC TIME PUZZLE
Pre-AP Activity

You have learned in Chapter 12 that the Earth is more than 4.5 billion years old—an amount of time so vast as to be almost incomprehensible. You also have learned that scientists rely on the geologic time scale when referring to moments in Earth's history. The time scale is divided into intervals of varying lengths based on the order in which certain rocks and fossils formed.

HOW THE TIME SCALE WAS DEVISED

Using fossil evidence and observations of geologic characteristics, scientists and naturalists as far back as Aristotle have tried to estimate Earth's age. The first attempts to base calculations on a rigorous scientific approach were begun in the 1880s. One of the leaders in this effort was English physicist William Thomson, better known as Lord Kelvin (1824–1907). Using mathematics, Lord Kelvin estimated that Earth was roughly 20–100 million years old. Kelvin based his calculations of Earth's age on the rate at which the molten Earth had supposedly cooled.

Kelvin's tremendous reputation was a key reason why this theory was widely accepted as fact. However, in 1913, a young English scientist, Arthur Holmes (1890–1965), proposed the first geologic time scale based on radioactivity. Using the latter to date rocks, Holmes estimated Earth's age at roughly 4 billion years—the first time anyone had suggested it could be that old. Holmes then used radioactivity to calibrate the various intervals of the geologic time scale. His calculations yielded a time scale that is very similar to the one used today.

HOW INTERVALS ARE DEFINED

Take a moment to review the geologic time scale on page 366. Note that each red X marks when a mass extinction took place. If you look at the location of each X you will notice that each mass extinction coincides with a boundary, or division, between two geologic periods. In fact, it is these major, catastrophic events that often define the intervals of geologic time periods.

- The Paleozoic era is framed by a dramatic radiation at its onset, and the equally stunning mass extinction that closed the era.
- The Mesozoic era was equally remarkable for tremendous changes in vegetation. The warm, moist climate facilitated the evolution and radiation of many plant forms, including flowering plants, as well as birds and fish.
- During the Cenozoic era, mammals underwent an explosive adaptive radiation, filling most of the niches left empty by the dinosaurs' demise. Some scientists think that the rate of extinction in recent years could mean that we are witnessing—and, in some cases, causing—another mass extinction.

SOLVE THE PUZZLE OF TIME

On the next page, use the provided hints and your textbook to complete the crossword puzzle on geologic time periods. Read each hint carefully before filling in your answers. If the word does not fit in the spaces provided, find one that does. Each term should appear only once in the puzzle.

Across

2. Today's animal phyla got their start
4. Supersized landmass . . . and a supersized extinction
7. "Recent life"
9. You're part of this
11. An era sandwiched by mass extinctions
12. Pterosaurs appeared
13. Provided the material for the fuel that early trains ran on
14. Earliest stop on an ornithologist's voyage back in time

Down

1. The first blossoms blossomed
3. Glaciers melted and plants came ashore
5. Longest era thus far
6. Marine invertebrate biodiversity's heyday
8. Bugs' beginning
10. Placentals and primates

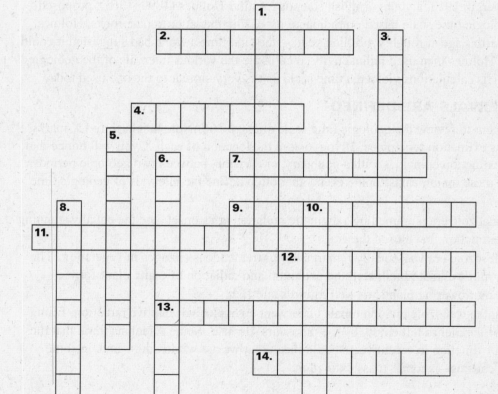

CHAPTER 12
The History of Life

THE FLORES HOBBIT CONTROVERSY
Pre-AP Activity

In Chapter 12 you have learned how scientists rely on rare fossils and other hard-to-find bits of evidence to piece together the history of hominid evolution. Now you will read about the current controversy over a recent find in a cave in Indonesia.

THE FLORES HOBBIT

In October, 2004, a team led by Peter Brown and Michael Morwood, both of Australia's University of New England, published a paper in the journal *Nature* that described a 18,000-year-old skeleton recovered from sediment inside a limestone cave on the island of Flores in Indonesia. The LB1 skeleton (named for the cave, Lian Bua) was remarkable because, while it belonged to an adult female it was only one meter tall and its brain volume was about one-third the size of the brain of a one-meter human. Other features, including the teeth and the reduced chin, suggested that this skeleton belonged to a species of hominid previously unknown to science. The scientists named the new species *Homo floresiensis,* after the island. The similarity between this new species and the tiny, elusive characters of J.R.R. Tolkein's books *The Hobbit* and *The Lord of the Rings* prompted scientists and the media to give the new hominid the nickname "Flores hobbit." Since then, the *Nature* paper's authors and their colleagues have also unearthed stone tools from Lian Bua, which suggests that *H. floresiensis* had tool-making abilities. Subsequent analysis of the shoulder joint of LB1 suggested that it was more like that of *H. erectus* than the modern human's. Dean Falk of Florida State University took casts of LB1's brain case and found that the shape and features of its brain resembled *Homo erectus* but it had rather advanced features more like modern humans', despite its small size.

But is LB1 really a new species? Brown and Morwood's team have recovered at least eight other skeletons of similar size from Lian Bua, but only LB1 had a skull. Is it possible that LB1 was simply a tool-wielding pygmy human, like the ones who currently live very close to Lian Bua, who happened to suffer from a known condition that made her head and brain abnormally small?

THE MICROCEPHALY HYPOTHESIS

Some experts were immediately skeptical that LB1 represented a new hominid species. These skeptics hypothesized that LB1 was a pygmy *Homo erectus* or *Homo sapiens.* A team of scientists from Indonesia, Australia, and Canada published a paper in 2006 that presented their analyses of the LB1 discovery. In the paper, Robert Eckhardt and other scientists argue that the brain size of LB1 is consistent with a condition called microcephaly that results in an abnormally small skull and brain. They point out that LB1's skull is asymmetrical, which further suggests a developmental abnormality. They also argue that the island of Flores is so small that it would have limited the population of such a hunter-gatherer species to the point where its genetic diversity would have been inadequate for long-term survival. Alan Thorne, one of the paper's authors, said that *Homo floresiensis* was indeed just like a hobbit: the "product of someone's imagination." Others have suggested that the microcephalic skulls which Dean Falk compared LB1 to were among the smallest that were available, and that Falk did not investigate the variety of forms that microcephaly can yield. They also argue that the stone tools found at Lian Bua are too sophisticated to have been made by any species other than *Homo sapiens.*

Brown, Morwood, and Falk have continued to argue that LB1 and the other skeletons do indeed represent a new species of hominid, and the *Nature* editor who published their work says that Thorne and the other authors of the microcephaly papers "cherry-picked" the evidence and failed to show that the combination of traits of LB1 matches that of any other hominid. This debate has, at times, become personal. After Peter Brown said Robert Eckhardt was "thick as a plank" in a magazine, Eckhardt had his wife measure his bare chest at a scientific meeting so that the audience could see that he was, in fact, thicker than two planks. To complicate matters, the Indonesian government has barred further excavation at Lian Bua.

Answer the questions below on a separate sheet of paper.

1. What evidence suggests that LB1 represents a new species? What evidence suggests that it is a microcephalic human? Create a T-chart to compare the evidence and the arguments.

2. One of the scientists involved in this debate said that there are usually more paleoanthropologists than there are bones to study. How does this story support that statement?

3. In the region surrounding Lian Bua, people have told folktales for many years about small, hairy, human-like creatures called Ebu Gogo that hid in Flores' limestone caves. Should the authors of the original *Nature* article use this story as evidence for their hypothesis? Explain.

4. How would the discovery of another 18,000-year-old skeleton on Flores just like LB1 affect this debate? What if the skeleton was identical but the skull was more humanlike?

5. What other type of evidence could help resolve this debate? Explain.

THE HISTORY OF LIFE
Vocabulary Practice

relative dating	epoch	Cenozoic
radiometric dating	nebula	primate
isotope	ribozyme	prosimian
half-life	cyanobacteria	anthropoid
index fossil	endosymbiosis	hominid
geologic time scale	Paleozoic	bipedal
era	Cambrian explosion	
period	Mesozoic	

A. Word Origins Circle the Greek and Latin word parts in each vocabulary term. Then use the Greek and Latin meanings to construct a very basic definition of the vocabulary word.

anthropo-	=	human	endo-	=	inside	-ped	=	foot
bi-	=	two	homo-	=	man	pro-	=	before
bio-	=	life	iso-	=	equal	simia-	=	ape
ceno-	=	new	meso-	=	middle	sym-	=	together
cyan-	=	greenish blue	paleo-	=	ancient	-zoic	=	geologic era

WORD	DEFINITION
1. isotope	
2. cyanobacteria	
3. endosymbiosis	
4. Paleozoic	
5. Mesozoic	
6. Cenozoic	
7. prosimian	
8. anthropoid	
9. hominid	
10. bipedal	

VOCABULARY PRACTICE, CONTINUED

B. Vector Vocabulary Define the words in the boxes. On the line across each arrow, write a phrase that describes how the words in the boxes are related to each other.

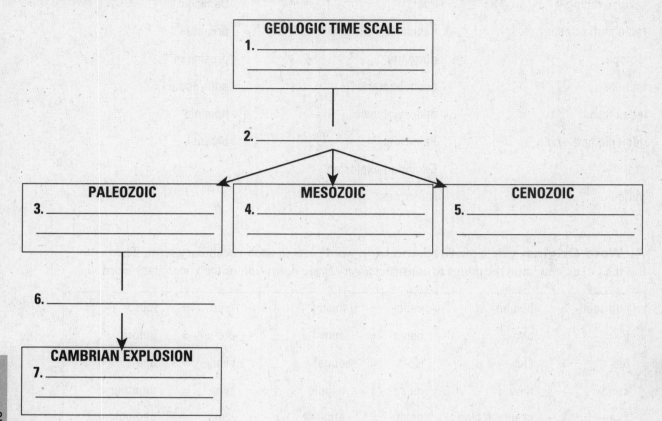

C. Categorize Words Write P next to words that can describe only primates that are not humans. Write H next to words that can describe only humans. Write B next to words that can describe both humans and other primates.

1. _____ prosimian   _____ anthropoid   _____ bipedal

   _____ hominid

VOCABULARY PRACTICE, CONTINUED

D. Who Am I? Choose among these terms to answer the riddles below:

relative dating	period	prosimian
radiometric dating	epoch	anthropoid
half-life	nebula	hominid
index fossil	ribozyme	
era	primate	

1. I am the amount of time it takes for half of an isotope in a sample to decay into a different element: _____

2. I am made up of epochs and am the most commonly used unit of time on the geologic time scale: _____

3. I am an RNA molecule that can catalyze specific chemical reactions: _____

4. I am a fossil that is used to determine the age of other fossils or rock layers: _____

5. I can be used to estimate when something lived based on comparing where it is found in a rock layer in relation to other rock layers: _____

6. I am the smallest unit of geologic time and I last several million years: _____

7. I am a member of a group of mammals that have flexible hands and feet and forward-looking eyes: _____

8. I am a member of the oldest living primate group and am small with big eyes: _____

9. I can estimate the actual age of a fossil or rock layer by using the decay rate of unstable isotopes in the sample that is tested: _____

10. I am made up of geologic periods and last tens to hundreds of millions of years: _____

11. I am a member of a group of primates that includes monkeys and apes, and my name means "humanlike": _____

12. I am a member of a group of primates whose only living species is modern humans, *Homo sapiens:* _____

13. I am a condensing cloud of gas and dust in space: _____

CHAPTER 12
The History of Life

E. Words in Context Answer the questions to show your understanding of the vocabulary words.

1. Which is an example of using **relative dating,** measuring the decay rate of isotopes or comparing the age of nearby rock layers?

   _____

2. Which is an example of a **ribozyme,** a ribosome with the traits of an enzyme, or RNA with the traits of an enzyme?

   _____

3. Which is a more likely place for **cyanobacteria** to live, within stromatolites in the ocean, or within particles in the air?

   _____

4. Which event occurred during the **Cambrian explosion,** the origin of the solar system, or the diversity of many animal species?

   _____

5. Does the theory of **endosymbiosis** describe the evolution of bacteria or of eukaryotic cells?

   _____

6. Does **radiometric dating** measure age using radio waves or isotopes of elements?

   _____

7. Does a **half-life** refer to the time it takes for an unstable isotope to decay, or the time it takes for half of a population to go extinct?

   _____

8. What is more likely to be an example of an **index fossil,** a trilobite found in a rock layer, or a woolly mammoth preserved in ice?

   _____

9. Is a **nebula** the possible beginning of Earth's formation, or a solid object from space that impacted early Earth?

   _____

10. Is an **era** better represented by the Paleozoic, or by the Cambrian explosion?

    _____

11. Is an **epoch** larger or smaller than an era?

    _____

UNIT
4 | MENDEL AND DARWIN
Unit Project

Gregor Mendel and Charles Darwin were contemporaries, that is, they both lived during the same period in history. Each of them profoundly advanced the science of biology, but they never met. Could some of Darwin's questions have been answered by Mendel's work? Could Mendel have better understood his own observations if he had communicated directly with Darwin? What if they had worked together? In this project, you will read and research the lives of both Mendel and Darwin, and then prepare a timeline and booklet of both of their lives.

- Research at least ten significant events in the lives of Darwin and Mendel. These may include birth, childhood, education, illnesses, obstacles in life, special accomplishments, writings and publications, honors, social influence, religious belief, attitudes, death, or legacy.

- In your research, you will take notes on 3" x 5" cards. Each card will briefly describe an important detail in the life of Darwin or Mendel. Prepare a set of cards for each scientist, and number your cards in chronological order. Note the source of your information on each card. Use these cards to complete your project. Bundle each set of cards neatly, and submit them along with your project.

- Cut a poster board in half lengthwise and tape the halves together, end to end. Using different colors, draw a timeline for each scientist's life, one over the other, on the same board. Label each line clearly with the full name of the scientist. Leave space between the timelines for writing dates. Be sure that the dates on the timeline line up. For example, the year 1850 should be at the same location on each timeline. You may illustrate your timelines with portraits of the scientists or other materials.

- Make a booklet to accompany your timelines. Fold several pieces of paper over together, and staple them in the fold line. Punch a hole in the upper left corner of the folded pages and tie a string or ribbon loop through the hole so you can hang it on a push pin next to your poster board. Number the pages. In the booklet, you will write details about each scientist's life. When finished, it will contain biographical information, the names and publication dates of their writings, reactions to their publications, and comparisons of their lives and work. Creativity is encouraged.

- Each timeline will mark at least 10 events that occurred in each scientist's life. On the timeline, label the year and the corresponding page number in your booklet where that event is discussed. All events marked on your timeline will be briefly discussed in your booklet. For example, Darwin boarded the *HMS Beagle* in 1831. By *1831* on your timeline, write the page number in your booklet where you tell about Darwin's voyage.

- At the end of your booklet, discuss what you think might have been the outcome if Darwin and Mendel had met and exchanged ideas. Would it have made a difference? Would they have even recognized that their work was related, or was there too much yet to be discovered in the sciences of genetics and evolution?

- Be as creative as possible, and be sure to make your timelines and booklet neat, organized, and easy to follow.

Mendel and Darwin Evaluation Rubric

Points will be assigned according to how well a task is done, as well as whether you have fully or only partially completed a task. Any task left undone will be assigned a zero. Your teacher will provide a timetable for this project.

Requirements	Maximum Points	Earned Points (teacher to fill in)
Note cards are neat, organized, and contain source references.	5	
Poster board contains two timelines, one for Darwin and one for Mendel. Lines are labeled clearly, with at least 10 significant dates for each.	10	
Timelines correspond in time, e.g., *1850* is in the same location on each line.	5	
Booklet is neatly folded and well made according to instructions.	5	
Timelines correctly identify page numbers in the booklet where specific information can be found.	5	
Minimum of 10 significant events in the lives of each scientist is detailed in the booklet.	25	
Booklet includes a brief comparative analysis of their lifestyles, works, and impacts on science.	20	
A discussion of a possible outcome if Darwin and Mendel had exchanged ideas is well reasoned, clear, and plausible.	15	
Timelines and booklet are neat, organized, and easy to follow.	10	
Rubric Score:	100 points	
Extra Credit (given at teacher's discretion):		
Map showing where Mendel and Darwin spent their lives, travels, and work is included. Locations are connected by a line, one color for Darwin and one for Mendel.	5	
Total Score:		

Teacher's Comments:

 # UNIT 4

MENDEL AND DARWIN
Unit Project Teacher Notes

Purpose: Understand, compare, and contrast the historical achievements, lives, and time of Charles Darwin and Gregor Mendel.

Overview: Students will research the lives of Charles Darwin and Gregor Mendel, comparing their lives and work. Students will
- research and take notes of the biographies of Darwin and Mendel
- prepare a timeline showing the significant dates in the lives of each scientist
- write a booklet that describes significant events on the timeline of each scientist, and compares and contrasts their lives and work

Preparation:
- Copy the project description and the rubric for students.
- Plan timetable.
- You may want to locate several appropriate Web sites that provide biographical information on Darwin and Mendel. Several Web sites are available that compare their lives and work by entering both of their names together as search words. Go to **ClassZone.com** for helpful resources and links.

Project Management:
- Assign the project at the beginning of Chapter 10.
- Have students read over the project sheet before beginning their research.
- Projects are completed outside of class and should take three weeks to complete.
- Projects may be done individually.
- Suggest and provide library references.
- Refer students to Chapter 6, Sections 6.3–6.6 and Chapter 7, Sections 7.1–7.2 in their textbook for references to Mendel.
- Have students check in weekly to monitor their progress.

Differentiation: This project can be adapted for various ability levels within the class.
- **Below Level students:** Students may complete this project by preparing only the timeline poster. Each timeline should be clearly labeled with dates and should include events and brief explanatory captions for each significant date.

Copyright © McDougal Littell/Houghton Mifflin Company.

UNIT 4
Evolution

Answer Key

Section 10.1

Study Guide

1. developed a classification system to group organisms by their similarities, that also reflects evolutionary relationships
2. suggested that species shared ancestors
3. contended that all living things were descended from a common ancestor and that more-complex forms of life arose from less-complex forms.
4. proposed that changes in physical characteristics could be inherited and were driven by environmental changes over time
5. they must be able to reproduce and have fertile offspring
6. Lamarck thought that greater use or disuse of a structure or organ would cause changes that could then be passed on to offspring.
7. different species could be produced with hybridization, showing that species can change

8. **Catastrophism:** the theory that natural disasters such as floods and volcanic eruptions have happened often during Earth's long history. These events have shaped landforms and caused species to become extinct. **Gradualism:** the principle that changes observed in landforms resulted from slow changes over a long period of time.
Uniformitarianism: the theory that the geologic processes that shape Earth are uniform through time.

9. fossils
10. evolution
11. catastrophism
12. uniformitarianism

13. Erasmus Darwin
14. Lamarck
15. Linnaeus
16. Buffon

Power Notes

Linnaeus: Developed a classification system for all types of organisms known at the time based upon their physical similarities.
Buffon: Proposed that species shared ancestors and suggested that Earth is much older than 6000 years.
E. Darwin: Proposed that all organisms descended from a common ancestor, and that more-complex forms of life arose from less-complex forms.
Lamarck: Proposed that all organisms evolved toward perfection and complexity and that structures became larger or smaller with use or disuse.
catastrophism: Natural disasters such as floods and volcanic eruptions have shaped landforms and caused species to become extinct.
gradualism: Changes in landforms resulted from slow changes over a long period of time.
uniformitarianism: The geologic processes that shape Earth are uniform through time.

Reinforcement

1. Examples include: species can change, species share ancestors, more-complex forms of life arose from less-complex forms, changes in physical changes could be inherited and were driven by environmental changes over time.
2. The theory of uniformitarianism combines the idea that changes on Earth are slow and gradual with the observation that these changes occur at a constant rate and are ongoing.

Section 10.2

Study Guide

1. interspecific variation
2. intraspecific variation
3. Galápagos Islands
4. that species may somehow be able to adapt to their surroundings

5. He thought modern animals might have some relationship to fossil forms
6. It would take much longer than 6000 years for the changes to occur between the fossil organisms he saw and their modern-day relatives.
7. Darwin saw that in geologic processes, great changes

can occur slowly, over a long period of time. He extended this insight to the evolution of organisms.

8. There are differences in shell shape, the edges of the shells, the lengths of the tortoises necks, the lengths of their legs.

9. variation
10. adaptation
11. adaptation
12. variation

Be Creative: First sketch should depict a bird with a strong, thick beak. Second sketch should depict a bird with a delicate-looking beak.

Power Notes

Variation: The difference in the physical traits of an individual from those of other individuals in the group to which it belongs.
Tortoise
example: Saddle-backed tortoises, which have long necks and legs, live in areas with a lot of tall plants. Domed tortoises, with shorter necks and legs, live in wet areas with short plants.
Finch
example: Finches with strong, thick beaks live in areas with a lot of large, hard-shelled nuts, while finches with more delicate beaks are found where insects or fruits are widely available.
Finch adaptation: A feature that allows an

organism to better survive in its environment.
Fossil evidence: Glyptodon, a giant extinct armadillo that resembled living armadillos. Also fossil shells of marine organisms high up in the mountains, showing great changes that occurred in the past.
Geologic evidence: Land that had been underwater was moved above sea level due to an earthquake, demonstrating that daily geologic processes can add up to a great change over a long period of time.

Reinforcement

1. A variation is a difference within an individual organism from the rest of the population. An adaptation is a feature that helps an organism survive in its environment. Over time, adaptations can become common in a population.
2. Examples include longer legs and necks on tortoises that live around higher vegetation, stronger beaks in finches that live in areas with lots of large, tough seeds.
3. Gradual geologic or biological changes can add up to cause great change over long periods of time.

Section 10.3

Study Guide

1. Darwin noticed breeders could produce a great amount of diversity in species.
2. If a trait is not heritable, it won't be passed down to offspring.
3. The traits are selected only if they give advantages to individuals in their present environment.
4. Human populations would grow geometrically if resources were unlimited. Instead, disease and a limited food supply kept the population smaller.

5. overproduction
6. variation
7. adaptation
8. descent with modification

9. sketch should reflect variation in a population
10. sketch should reflect overproduction
11. sketch should reflect an adaptation
12. sketch should reflect descent with modification over generations

13. increase
14. decrease

15. artificial selection
16. natural selection
17. fitness
18. heritability
19. population

Power Notes

Artificial selection: The process by which humans

change a species by breeding it for certain traits.

Heritability : The ability of a trait to be passed down from one generation to the next.

Struggle for survival: Populations would grow geometrically if resources were unlimited. Instead, disease and a limited food supply keep the population smaller.

Natural selection: A mechanism by which individuals that have inherited beneficial adaptations produce more offspring on average than do other individuals.

Variation: The heritable differences that exist in every population are the basis for natural selection.

Overproduction: Having many offspring increases the chance of survival but also results in competition for resources.

Adaptation: A certain variation that allows an individual to survive better than other individuals it competes against.

Descent with modification: Heritability of adaptations. More individuals will have the trait in every following generation, as long as the environmental conditions remain beneficial for the trait.

Reinforcement

1. traits that are selected appear in later generations

2. humans do the selecting of traits in artificial selection, while the environment is the selective agent in natural selection.

3. No, if the trait is not heritable, it will not be passed down to new generations

4. No. For natural selection to occur, traits that are advantageous for a certain environment must already exist in the population.

Section 10.4

Study Guide

1. **Fossils:** More primitive fossil organisms are in older layers, with more complex forms found in upper layers

2. **Geography:** Different ecosystems favor different traits and can establish separate populations that have a common ancestor

3. **Embryology:** Embryos of very different organisms that develop similarly provide evidence of a common ancestor

4. **Anatomy:** Homologous structures are features that are similar in structure but appear in different organisms and have different functions. They are evidence of a common ancestor

5. The tiny pelvic bones and hind limbs in many snakes, the wings of ostriches, and the human appendix

6. The ancestor of whales lived on land.

7. homologous structure
8. analogous structure
9. analogous structure
10. vestigial structure
11. homologous structure
12. analogous structure
13. vestigial structure

Sketch it Out: Students should match homologous structures directly between the two forelimbs.

Power Notes

Fossils: More primitive fossils are found in lower rock layers.

Geography: Island species most closely resemble species on the nearest mainland, and populations can show variations from one island to the next.

Embryology: Crab and barnacle larvae look identical, but have very different adult body forms. Likewise, embryos of vertebrates such as fish, birds, reptiles, and mammals look very similar

Homologous structures: Features that are similar in structure but appear in different organisms and have different functions.

Vestigial structures: Remnants of organs or structures that had a function in an early ancestor

Analogous structures: Structures that perform a similar function, but are not similar in origin.

Reinforcement

1. Geologists saw that the fossil organisms in older layers were more primitive than those found in younger, or newer layers. This supported Darwin's idea of descent with modification.
2. Island organisms can show a pattern of evolution as they adapt to different environments in separate island populations.
3. Similar features of embryos in very different organisms suggest evolution from a distant common ancestor.
4. homologous structures, vestigial structures

Section 10.5

Study Guide

1. most living things do not form into fossils after they die, and fossils have not been looked for in many areas of the world
2. *Basilosaurus isis*
3. They demonstrate the evolution of traits within groups as well as the common ancestors between groups.
4. The more related two organisms are, the more similar their DNA will be. Because there are thousands of genes in even simple organisms, DNA contains a huge amount of information on evolutionary history.
5. Pseudogenes no longer function but can change as they are carried along with

functional DNA through generations. Similarities between pseudogenes must come from a common ancestor.
6. Homeobox genes control the development of specific structures. Similar homeobox gene clusters are evidence of a common ancestor.
7. Similarities of proteins across organisms can be revealed by molecular fingerprinting, and are evidence of a common ancestor.
8. The theory of natural selection combined with genetics
9. Comparisons of milk protein genes confirm the fossil evidence that modern-day whales descended from land mammals
10. The basic principles of evolution are used in all the fields of biology
11. The study of fossils can provide new information and support current hypotheses about how evolution occurs.

Sketch It Out: Answers should reflect knowledge that *Pakicetus* lived on land and *Durodon* lived in water.

Power Notes

DNA sequence analysis: The more related two organisms are, the more similar their DNA will be.

Pseudogenes: No longer function but are still carried along with functional DNA. Like vestigial structures, they provide evidence of a common ancestor.
Homeobox genes: control the development of specific structures. Indicate a very distant common ancestor.
Protein comparisons: Comparing proteins in cells, called molecular fingerprinting, can indicate a common ancestor.

Reinforcement

1. It had the body of a whale but the limbs of an animal that lived on land.
2. The more similarities two organisms share, the more likely it is that they shared a common ancestor.
3. An understanding of evolution based on natural selection combined with genetic evidence.

Chapter 10

Data Analysis Practice

1. No, there does not appear to be a significant decrease in egg size in the Nahmint and Nanaimo Rivers due to the addition of captive bred salmon.
2. Yes, Robertson Creek shows a decrease in egg volume size between 1975 and 2000 that may be due to the addition of many captive bred salmon. However, the Quinsam River does not show a similar decrease.

3. Whether stocking the rivers with salmon bred in captivity affects egg size cannot be determined from the results of this study.

Pre-AP* Activity

LYSENKOISM: EVOLUTIONARY THEORY IN THE U.S.S.R.

1. Answers will vary. Capitalism was seen by Lysenko as a kind of social Darwinism. Lysenko thought that intraspecific competition and "survival of the fittest" would suggest that the rise of a bourgeois, wealthy class in a human population was natural. This would have severely undermined the communist ideology. By arguing that humans were not naturally competitive with one another, and that they were merely competitive with other species and other populations, he supported the idea that the working class could band together and create the type of society they viewed as ideal.

2. Answers will vary, but students should understand that science is about asking questions, formulating ideas and hypotheses, and then testing in a methodical, repeatable, unbiased manner. Anti-intellectualism in Stalin's Soviet Union went so far as to actually imprison and kill scientists

who were performing real scientific work.

3. Answers will vary, but students should write that scientists must not skew their methods or results in order to obtain a desired result. Lysenko is essentially justifying bias and ignoring the importance of unexpected results.

Pre-AP Activity

BIOINFORMATICS: SEQUENCING THE CLOCK GENE

1. 19 differences; 92.4% similar

2. Values are similar; scientists found that the sequences were 89% identical, which is only slightly lower than 92.4%. Since only a tiny segment is included here, we can expect differences.

3. Different codons can code for the same amino acid. So, even though the nucleotide sequences are different, they may in fact code for the same amino acid.

4. *Sample Answer:*
(1) AUG-CUU-UUU-ACU-GUU-ACU-UGU-AGU-AAA-AUG
(2) AUG-CUC-UUC-ACC-GUC-AGC-UGC-AGC-AAG-AUG
(3) AUG-CUA-UUU-ACA-GUA-AGU-UGU-AGU-AAA-AUG

Vocabulary Practice

A. Stepped-Out Vocabulary

1. Difference in the physical traits of an individual from those of other individuals.

2. Homologous

3. sample answer: does not provide evidence of common descent, examples include wings of insects and birds.

4. Vestigial structures; Remnants of organs or structures that had a function in an early ancestor.

B. Compound Word Puzzle

1. species; sample answer: all of the same kind

2. adaptation; sample answer: allows an organism to better survive in its environment

3. natural selection; sample answer: mechanism by which populations evolve

4. population; a community of individuals of the same species

C. Do-It Yourself Matching

1. Sample answer: biological change over time

2. Sample answer: ability to produce offspring

3. Sample answer: theory that natural disasters caused great change on Earth

4. Sample answer: theory that change on Earth occurs slowly

5. Sample answer: processes of change that can be seen today also caused change in the past

6. Sample answer: humans select traits for breeding

7. Sample answer: the environmental conditions cause certain traits to be more advantageous than others
8. Sample answer: study of fossils
9. Sample answer: study of the distribution of organisms across Earth
10. Sample answer: able to be passed down to offspring

D. Find the Odd Word
1. fitness; paleontology is the study of fossils
2. biogeography; something must be heritable to undergo artificial selection
3. catastrophism; uniformitarianism incorporates the theory of gradualism plus the idea that what happened in the past can be observed occurring today
4. analogous structure; homologous and vestigial structures are both evidence of common descent
5. vestigial structure; there must be variation in a population for adaptation to occur
6. catastrophism; natural selection is a mechanism by which evolution occurs

E. Crossword Puzzle
Across
1. uniformitarianism
5. vestigial structures
8. fossil
10. analogous structures
11. catastrophism
12. analogous structures
13. natural selection
14. adaptation

Down
2. artificial selection
3. gradualism
4. evolution
6. species
7. fitness

Section 11.1
Study Guide
1. genetic variation
2. A wide range of phenotypes increases the likelihood that some individuals will have traits that allow them to survive in new environmental conditions.
3. gene pool
4. the combined alleles of all individuals in a population
5. allele frequency
6. dividing the number of times an allele occurs by the total number of alleles
7. Can produce new alleles. Mutations in reproductive cells can be passed on to offspring.
8. Forms new genetic combinations that are passed on to offspring.
9. New genetic information can be introduced into populations when species mate with other closely-related species.
10. it contains all of the genes/alleles of all the individuals in a population
11. how common a certain allele is in a gene pool

Be Creative: Share the most creative responses with the class.

Power Notes
Genetic Variation
Why it's beneficial: Results in phenotypic variation which increases the likelihood that some individuals can survive a change in the environment.
How it's stored in a population: as alleles in a gene pool
How it's measured: with allele frequencies; how common each allele is in the population
Two main sources
Mutation: a change in a DNA sequence which can form a new allele
Recombination: new allele combinations can form during meiosis, when each parent's alleles are arranged in new ways in the production of gametes

Reinforcement
1. all the alleles of all the individuals in the population
2. with allele frequencies
3. Mutation can form new alleles and recombination can form new combinations of alleles.
4. Genetic variation is the basis for phenotypic variation, and different phenotypes (traits) are necessary in order for natural selection to "select" those that are best suited to the environment.

Section 11.2

Study Guide

1. graph that shows the frequency of each phenotype for a trait in a population
2. how common each phenotype is in the population; whether or not the population is undergoing natural selection for that trait
3. a normal distribution or a bell-shaped curve

Phenotypic Distribution:
Graph should resemble a bell-shaped curve. X-axis should be labeled "range" or "range of phenotypes"; y-axis should be labeled "frequency." Mean phenotype should be labeled in the center of the curve, which is also the peak of the curve.

4. Favors phenotypes at one extreme of a trait's range; graph should show a normal distribution shifted either to the right or left.
5. Favors intermediate phenotypes/selects against phenotypes at both extremes; graph should show distribution with sharp peak in center at the mean.
6. Favors phenotypes at both extremes of a trait's range/selects against intermediate phenotypes; graph should show distribution with one peak at each extreme.

7. allele frequencies
8. stabilizing
9. disruptive
10. directional

Power Notes

Normal distribution: distribution in which frequency is highest near the mean value and decreases steadily toward each extreme end of the range
A population follows a normal distribution when: that population is not under natural selection for the trait
Graph: Should resemble a bell-shaped curve; may label "mean" in center.
Microevolution: observable change in allele frequencies of a population over time
Directional selection: favors phenotypes at one extreme of a trait's range; graph should show normal distribution curve shifted over to the right or left; *Example:* drug-resistance in bacterial populations
Stabilizing selection: favors intermediate phenotypes; graph should show narrower distribution with peak in the middle (at the mean phenotype); *Example:* size of gall fly galls
Disruptive selection: favors phenotypes at both extremes of a trait's range; graph should show two peaks, one near each extreme phenotype, with low frequency in the middle (at the mean phenotype);

Example: body color in male lazuli buntings

Reinforcement

1. all the phenotypes in a trait's range and how common each one is in the population
2. when the trait is not undergoing natural selection
3. a distribution in which the frequency is highest near the mean value and decreases toward each extreme
4. directional selection: selects for one extreme phenotype; stabilizing selection: selects for the mean phenotype; disruptive selection: selects for both extreme phenotypes

Section 11.3

Study Guide

1. emigrates
2. immigrates
3. gene pools

4. Changes in allele frequencies through genetic drift are due to chance alone, while changes in allele frequencies through natural selection are the result of specific environmental pressures.

Y Diagram: Bottleneck effect—results from drastic reduction in population size; Founder effect—results from a small number of individuals colonizing a new area; Both—involve genetic drift in a small population, resulting in a decrease in genetic variation over time

5. Smaller populations are more likely to be affected by chance events, since there are not as many alleles to "balance out" random changes in allele frequencies.

6. The loss of genetic diversity decreases the chance that some individuals will be able to survive new environmental conditions, and genetically harmful alleles can build up in the population due to chance alone.

7. Males produce many sperm continuously and females are much more limited in the number offspring they can produce in each reproductive cycle.

8. Certain male traits increase mating success based on the choosiness of females for potential mates.

9. Intrasexual, intersexual

Vocabulary Check: Gene flow—could show two "populations" of shapes with arrows going back and forth in between them; Bottleneck effect—could show bottle being held upside-down with only a few of pieces of its contents spilling out; Founder effect—could show a few shapes that have founded a small "population" next

to the original, larger population

Power Notes

Gene Flow:

Definition: movement of alleles from one population to another
How it works: when animals move from one population to another and breed in the new population; when spores or seeds of plants or fungi are spread to new areas
Lots of gene flow results in: similar populations (genetically)
Limited gene flow results in: different populations (genetically) that could evolve into different species

Genetic Drift:

Definition: changes in allele frequencies due to chance alone
How it works: small populations are more likely to be affected by chance; due to chance some alleles may increase in frequency while others may decrease and even become eliminated from the population.
Bottleneck effect: genetic drift that occurs after an event drastically reduces the size of a population

Founder Effect:

genetic drift that occurs after a small number of individuals colonize a new area
Negative effects: population loses genetic variation, so population is less likely

to have some individuals that will be able to adapt to a changing environment; harmful alleles may become more common due to chance alone

Sexual Selection:

Definition: process in which certain traits increase mating success and therefore become more common in the population
How it works: females preferentially mate with males that display certain traits, so those traits get passed on to offspring and can become more exaggerated each generation
Intrasexual: competition/fighting among males for females
Intersexual: males display certain traits to attract females

Reinforcement

1. When individuals leave one population and join a new one, their alleles are lost from their old population and are added to the new population.

2. In smaller populations, there are less alleles to "balance out" the effect of random changes in allele frequencies.

3. Traits that increase mating success for males are selected for by females, and therefore get passed on from generation to generation and can become more and more exaggerated.

Section 11.4

Study Guide

1. allele frequencies
2. very large population (so genetic drift does not occur); no emigration or immigration (so there is no gene flow); no mutations (so no new alleles are introduced into gene pool); random mating (so there is no sexual selection); no natural selection.
3. biologists can (1) study the degree in which real populations are evolving and (2) better understand the five factors that can lead to evolution

4. $p^2 + 2pq + q^2 = 1$

5. p^2, frequency of dominant homozygous genotype; $2pq$, frequency of heterozygous genotype; q^2, frequency of recessive homozygous genotype; p, frequency of dominant allele; q, frequency of recessive allele

6. single-gene traits in simple, dominant-recessive systems
7. the phenotype and allele frequencies; specifically the phenotype frequency of the recessive homozygotes (q^2), from which the frequency of the recessive allele (q) can be calculated
8. the population is not in H-W equilibrium for the trait, which means one or more of the conditions are not met, which means the population is evolving
9. **Genetic drift:** in small populations, allele frequencies can change due to chance alone. **Gene flow:** migration of individuals results in the movement of alleles among populations, which changes allele frequencies. **Mutation:** new alleles can form due to mutation, which changes allele frequencies. **Sexual selection:** alleles associated with traits that increase mating success can increase in frequency. **Natural selection:** alleles associated with traits that increase survival and reproductive success can increase in frequency.

10. allele frequencies

Power Notes

Hardy-Weinberg Equilibrium: equilibrium state in which genotype frequencies in a population stay the same from generation to generation *Why it is important:* comparing real data with that predicted by the equilibrium model; framework for testing factors that can lead to evolution

1. very large population
2. no emigration or immigration
3. no mutations
4. random mating
5. no natural selection

Hardy-Weinberg Equation:
$p^2 + 2pq + q^2 = 1$
What it means: frequency of dominant homozygotes + frequency of heterozygotes + frequency of recessive homozygotes = 1 (or any reminder of meanings of variables or meaning of equation) How it's used: to predict genotype frequencies of populations in Hardy-Weinberg equilibrium for simple, dominant-recessive traits

1. genetic drift
2. gene flow
3. mutation
4. sexual selection
5. natural selection

Reinforcement

1. If no forces of evolution act on a population, the allele frequencies will remain constant.
2. very large population, no emigration or immigration, no mutations, random mating, and no natural selection
3. genotype frequencies
4. the population is evolving/at least one of the conditions for equilibrium is not met
5. At least one of the five factors that can lead to evolution is likely to be acting on a population at any given time.

Section 11.5

Study Guide

1. gene flow
2. gene pools
3. environments, genetic drift
4. mate
5. speciation, species
6. mutation

7. behavioral, geographic, and temporal barriers
8. **Behavioral isolation:** changes in behavior between two populations can act as barriers which prevent mating. Examples: Fruit flies in the ds2 experiment which evolved different pheromones, firefly species with different flash patterns. **Geographic isolation:** physical barriers can divide populations. Example: Isthmus of Panama divides populations of marine species in the Atlantic and Pacific Oceans. **Temporal isolation:** differences in mating periods or times of day when individuals are active can prevent mating between populations. Example: Plant species that shed pollen during different times of the year.

9. the rise of two or more species from one existing species
10. temporal
11. behavioral
12. geographic

Power Notes

Reproductive isolation: occurs when members of different populations are no longer physically able to mate successfully with one another

Speciation: the rise of two or more species from one existing species

1. behavioral barriers/isolation: differences in courtship of mating behaviors prevents reproduction between populations
2. geographic barriers/isolation: physical barriers that divide a population into two or more groups
3. temporal barriers/isolation: timing of reproductive periods or courtship prevents reproduction between populations

Reinforcement

1. There must be no gene flow between them.
2. when individuals from two populations are no longer able to mate successfully
3. If two populations are isolated, they can become more and more genetically different over time. If they become so different that they are no longer able to mate successfully, the two populations are considered to be different species.
4. behavioral isolation: differences in courting or mating behaviors prevent mating between populations; geographic

isolation: physical barriers such as mountain ranges prevent mating between populations; temporal isolation: differences in the timing of reproductive activity prevents mating between populations.

Section 11.6

Study Guide

1. Main Idea: Evolution through natural selection is not random.
2. Natural selection has direction: Environmental pressures can "push" a population's traits in a certain direction.
3. Its effects are cumulative: The effects of natural selection add up over time, and the alleles associated with advantageous traits add up over many generations in the gene pool.
4. Convergent evolution: Distantly-related species can evolve similar traits while adapting to similar environments.
5. Divergent evolution: Closely-related species can evolve different traits while adapting to different environments.

6. beneficial relationship: two or more species evolve in a cooperative way, each evolving characteristics that are beneficial to the other; Example: stinging ants and bull-thorn acacia
7. evolutionary arms race: two or more species evolve

in a competitive way, each evolving characteristics that put some type of evolutionary pressure on the other; Example: crabs and murex snails.

8. background extinction: caused by local changes in the environment, such as changes in food supply; outcome is that a few species may go extinct in localized area

9. mass extinction: caused by catastrophic events on a global level, such as an ice age; outcome is that many species go extinct around the world in a relatively short period of time

10. speciation , change
11. descendent
12. environments or opportunities

13. Convergent evolution is two unrelated species "coming together" by becoming increasingly similar; divergent evolution is two related species "branching out" by becoming increasingly different.

14. Species evolve together, in response to changes in one another.

15. The equilibrium between speciation and extinction is "periodically interrupted" by episodes of rapid speciation.

Power Notes

Convergent Evolution: evolution toward similar characteristics in unrelated species

Divergent Evolution: evolution toward different characteristics in closely related species

Coevolution: process in which species evolve in response to changes in each other

Beneficial Relationships: both species receive benefits from the other as a result of adaptations that each species has evolved over many generations

Evolutionary Arms Races: both species respond to competitive pressure from the other through adaptations over many generations

Extinction: elimination of a species from Earth

Background Extinction: occur randomly but at a very low rate; usually affect only a few species in a small area; can be caused by local changes in the environment

Mass Extinction: rare but very intense; can operate at global level and destroy many species; caused by catastrophic events such as ice age

Patterns in Speciation

Punctuated Equilibrium: episodes of speciation occur suddenly in geologic time and are followed by long periods of little evolutionary change.

Adaptive Radiation: diversification of one ancestral species into many descendent species, usually adapted to a wide range of environments

Reinforcement

1. it can have direction and its effects add up over time
2. divergent evolution
3. Background extinctions occur at low, constant rate and are due to local changes in the environment; mass extinctions occur suddenly and rapidly in geologic time due to globally catastrophic events and can kill thousands of species.
4. Speciation occurs suddenly and rapidly in geologic time and is followed by long periods with relatively little evolutionary change.

Chapter 11

Data Analysis Practice

1. The females were most attracted to the normal tail. The all-black coloration still attracted females, but not as much as the normal tail. The all-yellow tail attracted females the least of the three.
2. Fewer females might mate with this fish.

Pre-AP Activity

CALCULATING GENE FREQUENCIES

1. $f(S) = [(2 \times 1530 + 568)] / 2236 = 874 / 2236 = \mathbf{0.39}$; $f(s) = [(2 \times 397) + 568] / 2236 = 1362 / 2236 = \mathbf{0.61}$
2. Yes. The frequency of the short-hair allele went down and the frequency of the long-hair allele

went up. Long-haired cats must have some type of selective advantage in their environment. Speculation will vary. Perhaps temperatures dropped and short-haired cats died, or long-haired cats mated only with one another and did so more successfully than short-haired cats, or short-haired cats suffered more from predation or disease.

3. Once you have calculated the frequency of one allele, you can calculate the other by subtracting the first from 1. For example, if $f(S) = 0.65$, then $f(s) = 1 - 0.65 = 0.35$.

4. Genetic diversity has been reduced, which could mean that the population as a whole may be less resilient to future changes to the environment or other factors. The less diverse a population is, the less likely it is that there will be at least some individuals who will be able to survive a change in the environment.

Pre-AP Activity

EVOLUTIONARY ADVANTAGES OF SEXUAL REPRODUCTION

1. In the first two scenarios, the asexual organisms produced more offspring per adult and the offspring had all of the parent's genes, signifying an obvious advantage over the sexual organisms,

which had to mate with each other and could only pass on 50% of their genes to an offspring. In the computer simulation, the recombination that occurs in sexual reproduction proved to be an advantage because it allowed for greater genetic variety to arise much faster that it possibly can in an asexual population. This genetic diversity served as a source of traits (in this case, receptors) that could fight disease. The asexual population could not evolve defenses against disease as quickly as the sexual population could.

2. *Sample Answer:* The Red Queen hypothesis describes the reciprocal "arms race" that occurs between parasites and hosts, and other antagonistic pairs (predator and prey, virus and host, etc). Essentially, as the parasite evolves new ways to attack its hosts, the hosts must rely on new traits in order to fend off or withstand the parasite. A new trait could evolve through mutation in an asexual organism that might allow it to survive infestation, but because that organism does not mate, that trait will only be passed on to its own offspring. For other, unrelated asexual individuals to get that trait, that trait must arise through mutation in

their lineage. In sexual organisms, mating and recombination allows traits to be passed on through multiple lineages through generations, thereby giving those organisms the beneficial defense mechanism. Because the parasite (or other threat) is also evolving, it's own evolution is likely to match or exceed the ability of the asexual organism.

Vocabulary Practice

A. Who Am I?

1. temporal isolation
2. normal distribution
3. geographic isolation
4. Hardy-Weinberg equilibrium
5. punctuated equilibrium
6. behavioral isolation

B. Word Origins

1. evolving together
2. evolution in which two species "come together" becoming more similar, from different directions
3. evolution in which two species evolve in different directions from a common point, or common ancestor
4. evolution on a small scale

C. Choose the Correct Word

1. stabilizing selection
2. normal distribution
3. directional selection
4. disruptive selection
5. geographic isolation
6. reproductive isolation
7. behavioral isolation
8. temporal isolation

9. coevolution
10. convergent evolution
11. divergent evolution
12. microevolution

D. Do-It Yourself Matching

1. Sample answer: many species evolving from one
2. Sample answer: all the alleles in a population
3. Sample answer: favors one extreme phenotype
4. Sample answer: favors the intermediate phenotype
5. Sample answer: favors both extreme phenotypes
6. Sample answer: the rise of a new species

E. Analogies

1. punctuated equilibrium
2. genetic drift
3. normal distribution
4. extinction
5. gene flow
6. allele frequency
7. gene pool
8. geographic isolation

Section 12.1

Study Guide

1. Amber preserved fossil
2. Natural cast
3. Record of the activity of an organism, such as a nest or footprints.
4. Minerals are deposited around a hard structure and may replace the structure.
5. Preserved remains
6. Pressure from additional sediment compresses the body.
7. Minerals replace all the hard structures.

8. Both relative dating and radiometric dating are used to determine the age of a fossil or rock layer.
9. Relative dating is an estimate based on the fossil or rock layer's location, whereas radiometric dating determines a fossil's absolute, or actual, age.
10. As an isotope of an element decays, it can transform into a different element. Because the decay rate of many radioactive isotopes are known, the proportion between an original element and its product isotope allows scientists to determine when that rock layer was formed.
11. 25 percent

12. radiometric dating
13. isotope
14. half-life
15. relative dating

Power Notes

Permineralization: when minerals in water are deposited around or replace the hard structure.
Natural casts: when flowing water removes all of the original bone or tissue, leaving just an impression that minerals then fill in.
Trace fossils: record the activity of an organism, including nests, burrows, and footprints.
Amber-preserved fossils: Organisms that become trapped in tree resin that

hardens after the tree gets buried underground.
Preserved remains: when an entire organism becomes incased in material such as ice, ash, or immersed in a bog
Relative dating: estimates the time during which an organism lived by comparing the placement of fossil of that organism with the placement of fossils in other layers of rock.
Radiometric dating: technique that uses the natural decay rate of unstable isotopes found in materials in order to calculate the age of the material.
Isotopes: atoms of an element that have the same number of protons but a different number of neutrons. (Students should shade in 6 protons, 6 neutrons for carbon-12 and 6 protons, 8 neutrons for carbon-14).
Half-life: the amount of time it takes for half of an isotope in a sample to decay into a different element, its product isotope. (Students should draw in a descending line of graph from 100% isotope remaining to less than 6.25 remaining at end of graph. Points should intersect at each mark of the x and y-axes.)

Reinforcement

1. Minerals directly replace tissue in a permineralized fossil. In a natural cast, the tissues decay away, leaving

just an impression that then is eventually filled in by minerals.

2. Specific environmental conditions must be present at the time of the organism's death in order for its remains to be fossilized.

3. Relative dating provides an estimate of when an organism lived or rock layer was formed, whereas radiometric dating measures the actual age of the fossil or rock layer.

Section 12.2

Study Guide

1. Index fossils are used as markers to identify a particular layer of rock wherever it is found.

2. Common, easy to identify, found widely around the world, existed for a relatively brief time.

3. Paleozoic Era
4. Mesozoic Era
5. Cenozoic Era
6. Permian Period
7. Carboniferous Period
8. Cambrian Period
9. Jurassic Period
10. Triassic Period
11. Quaternary Period

12. epoch
13. period
14. era
15. era
16. epoch
17. period
18. period
19. era
20. period

21. era
22. ancient life
23. middle life
24. recent life

25. The geologic time scale organizes Earth's history by major changes or events, using evidence from fossil and geologic records.

Power Notes

Index fossil
definition: Fossils of organisms that existed only during specific spans of time over large geographic areas.
characteristics: common, easy to identify, found widely around the world, only existed for a relatively brief time.
example: fusulinids, trilobites
nonexample: anything that is rare to find or that are only found in a certain region.

Geologic time scale
Representation of the history of Earth that is organized by major changes or events.
Eras: Last tens to hundreds of millions of years and consist of two or more periods.
Periods: Most commonly used units of time, lasting tens of millions of years.
Epochs: The smallest units of time, lasting several million years.

1. Cenozoic era: Evolution of primates, diversification of

mammals, flowering plants. Continues today.

2. Mesozoic era: Evolution and extinction of dinosaurs, evolution of ferns and cycads, and mammals.

3. Paleozoic era: All existing animal phyla developed, earliest land plants arose.

Reinforcement

1. If a rock layer contains this type of index fossil, its relative age can be determined more precisely.

2. to organize Earth's history by major changes or events that have occurred

3. Cenozoic era

4. mass extinctions

Section 12.3

Study Guide

1. Earth is billions of years old, and the conditions of the early planet and its atmosphere were very different from those of today.

2. **Heat released by:** Impacts from space debris

3. **Heat released by:** radioactive decay of elements within Earth

4. **Atmosphere made of:** Ammonia, water vapor, methane, carbon dioxide

5. **Absent in Atmosphere:** oxygen

6. **Eon name:** Hadeon

7. **Energy provided by:** solar radiation

8. **Energy provided by:** lightning

9. Miller-Urey

10. more than 90 amino acids have been identified from this meteorite
11. Iron-sulfide bubbles hypothesis
12. spontaneously form in nature and could have formed the first true cell membranes
13. Ribozymes are RNA that can catalyze their own reactions without the additional enzymes that are needed for DNA replication.
14. nebula
15. ribozyme

Power Notes

Miller-Urey experiment: Demonstrated that organic compounds could be made by passing an electrical current, to simulate lightning, through a closed system that held a mixture of gases.

Meteorite hypothesis: Amino acids may have arrived on Earth through meteorite or asteroid impacts.

Iron-sulfide bubbles hypothesis: Biological molecules combined in compartments of chimneylike structures on the ocean floor. The compartments acted as the first cell membranes.

Lipid membrane hypothesis: Lipid spheres, or liposomes, could form around a variety of organic molecules, acting as early cell membranes.

Ribozymes: RNA molecules that can catalyze specific chemical reactions. May have been the first genetic material of cells.

Reinforcement

1. computer models and space observations
2. A mixture of gases acted as the early atmosphere, and a electric current represented lightning.

Section 12.4

Study Guide

1. By depositing minerals and by giving oxygen off as a by-product of photosynthesis.
2. Cyanobacteria existed as long as 3.5 billion years ago, which also suggests that oxygen was present on Earth at that time.
3. eukaryotes
4. nucleus
5. aerobic
6. cell
7. Simple infectious prokaryotic cells were taken up by larger prokaryotes.
8. Over generations, bacteria evolved as mitochondria or chloroplasts.
9. In the theory of endosymbiosis, chloroplasts are considered the descendants of cyanobacteria. An early infectious cyanobacteria may have entered a larger prokaryote, and after many generations evolved as

a chloroplast in an early eukaryote.

10. Producing many offspring quickly.
11. Genetic variation allows a population to adapt quickly to new conditions.
12. cyanobacteria
13. endosymbiosis
14. Answers will vary. Examples include endotherm, endoplasmic reticulum, endorphin, endorse, endospore.
15. Cyanobacteria live in aquatic systems and can photosynthesize.

Power Notes

Cyanobacteria: bacteria that can carry out photosynthesis; changed Earth by

1. depositing minerals in the form of stromatolites
2. producing oxygen as a by-product of photosynthesis

Endosymbiosis: A relationship in which one organism lives within the body of another, and both benefit from the relationship.

1. Early mitochondria and chloroplasts were once simple prokaryotic cells that were taken up by larger prokaryotes.
2. Instead of being digested, some of the larger prokaryotes may have survived inside the larger ones.

3. The smaller prokaryote could have given the larger cell energy or sugars, while the larger cell could have provided a stable environment and nutrients to the smaller cells. (Sketches should reflect a bacterium separate from a larger cell, the bacterium being taken in by a larger cell, and the bacterium completely within the larger cell.)

Reinforcement

1. Oxygen was not present on early Earth until it was produced by photosynthesizing organisms.
2. they can photosynthesize
3. eukaryotic cells
4. Having DNA and ribosomes are characteristics of independent organisms, although mitochondria and chloroplasts are organelles within a cell. It supports the theory that they evolved from smaller single-celled organisms.

Section 12.5

Study Guide

1. four-legged vertebrates such as amphibians became common
2. 70 percent of land animal species at the time became extinct by the period's end
3. dinosaurs roamed Earth
4. earliest crocodiles arose

5. ichthyosaurs, marine reptiles, dominated the oceans
6. Mammals radiated during the Cenozoic era.
7. placental mammals evolved and diversified
8. monotremes, mammals that lay eggs, evolved and diversified
9. earliest ancestors of modern humans evolved

10. Mesozoic
11. Paleozoic
12. Cambrian explosion
13. Cenozoic
14. Cambrian explosion
15. Mesozoic
16. Cenozoic
17. Paleozoic
18. Paleozoic
19. Mesozoic
20. Cenozoic

Power Notes

Paleozoic
years: 544 million years ago—248 million years ago
major events: Multicellular organisms first appeared. Members of every major animal group evolved. A huge mass extinction occurred at the end of the era.
Cambrian explosion: the Cambrian period. A huge diversity of animal species evolved.
Mesozoic
years: 248 million years ago—65 million years ago.
known as: Age of Reptiles
major events: mammals first appeared crocodiles and dinosaurs arose. A

mass extinction occurred, and dinosaurs became extinct.
Cenozoic
years: 65 million years ago—present
major events: placental mammals and monotremes evolved and diversified, primates evolved.

Reinforcement

1. because so many life forms evolved during this time period
2. the mammals
3. the dinosaurs

Section 12.6

Study Guide

1. anthropoid
2. hominoid
3. prosimians
4. Old World monkeys
5. New World monkeys
6. gibbons
7. orangutans
8. hominids
9. gorillas

10. *Australopithecus* and *Homo*
11. *Homo habilis*
12. *Homo neanderthalensis*

13. there is a steady trend of increasing sophistication and usefulness of tools
14. Laboratory studies that compared DNA sequences of more than 200 genes affecting brain size in both rodents and primates.

15. hominids
16. prosimians
17. anthropoid
18. primate

19. prosimian
20. hominids
21. prosimian
22. anthropoid

Power Notes

Primates: mammals with flexible hands and feet, forward-looking eyes, and enlarged brains relative to body size.

Prosimians: oldest living primate group. Mostly small and nocturnal.

Anthropoids: humanlike primates

Hominids: primates that walk upright, have long lower limbs, thumbs that oppose the other four fingers, and relatively large brains.

bipedal: can walk on two legs

1. New World monkeys
2. lesser apes
3. humans

Reinforcement

1. Physical and molecular similarities
2. They are small and nocturnal
3. Anthropoid and hominid
4. Able to walk on two feet or legs
5. Fossil evidence

Chapter 12

Data Analysis Practice

1. Students should determine the interval for the x-axis as follows: 2000 (highest value) -1600 (lowest value) = 400. 400 ÷ 5 = 80. 80 should be rounded up to 100 or down to 50. Students should determine the interval for the y-axis as follows: 140 (highest value) - 0 (lowest value) = 140. 140 ÷ 5 = 28. 28 can be rounded up to 30 or 50, or down to 25.
2. The x-axis would be too long.

Pre-AP Activity

GEOLOGIC TIME PUZZLE

2. Cambrian
4. Permian
7. Cenozoic
9. Quaternary
11. Mesozoic
12. Triassic
13. Carboniferous
14. Jurassic

1. Cretaceous
3. Silurian
5. Paleozoic
6. Ordovician
8. Devonian
10. Tertiary

Pre-AP Activity

THE FLORES HOBBIT CONTROVERSY

1. Student's T-charts should list the following evidence for *Homo floresiensis*: LB1's features are a unique combination, unlike any seen in modern humans or other hominids (small head, small but somewhat advanced brain, shoulder like *H. erectus)*; and for the microcephaly hypothesis: brain size and skull's asymmetrical shape are like that of a small microcephalic human, and the tools are too sophisticated to have been made by a nonhuman.
2. Only one skull was found in Lian Bua, which means that it is the only skull that could be studied and compared to other hominid bones or fossils.
3. No. A story is not hard evidence. A story can give someone a new idea or point them in a direction, but a story alone does not prove or disprove anything.
4. If the new skeleton and skull looked like LB1, it would help support the hypothesis that these finds represent a new species. If the new skeleton matched the others but the skull was more like a human's, it would support the hypothesis that LB1 was a microcephalic human, similar in size to pygmy humans.
5. DNA. It could be compared to DNA of humans and other primates to determine if LB1 is a distinct species.

Vocabulary Practice

A. Word Origins

1. atoms of the same element that have an equal number of protons
2. greenish blue bacteria
3. two organisms living together with one inside of the other
4. ancient geologic era
5. middle geologic era
6. new geologic era
7. existed before the apes

8. humanlike
9. manlike
10. two-footed

B. Vector Vocabulary

1. represents Earth's history
2. can be broken down into eras known as
3. multicellular organisms first appeared
4. called the age of reptiles
5. mammals radiated, most recent era
6. the earliest part is known as
7. when a huge diversity of life evolved

C. Categorize Words

1. prosimian, P; anthropoid, B; hominid, H; bipedal, B.

D. Who Am I?

1. half-life
2. period
3. ribozyme
4. index fossil
5. relative dating
6. epoch
7. primate
8. prosimian
9. radiometric dating
10. era
11. anthropoid
12. hominid
13. nebula

E. Words in Context

1. comparing nearby rock layers
2. RNA
3. stromatolites
4. diversity of animal species
5. eukaryotic cells
6. isotopes
7. isotope to decay
8. trilobite
9. beginning of Earth's formation
10. Paleozoic

11. smaller